TSUNEO SANDA

CONTENTS

Published 2009.
Published by Pedigree Books Limited, Beech Hill House, Walnut Gardens, Exeter, Devon EX4 4DH.
www.pedigreebooks.com Email: books@pedigreegroup.co.uk

GREETINGS

Greetings, my young Padawan, and welcome to this special guide to the most adventurous and exciting events in the history of the universe.

A long time ago, in a galaxy far, far away, a Chosen One was born. This single event set in motion a series of events that would, in time, destroy an entire Order, tear families apart and ravage the stars with war and terror.

Before you begin to explore how these events came to pass, and what became of the people who were caught up in them, you must first enter into the ancient Jedi Order and become a Padawan learner. Your first assignment is to complete the form on the opposite page.

In the coming pages you will face many more challenges. Each of these should be met with courage and patience. Follow the examples of the great Jedi who have gone before you, and you too will one day be a fully-fledged Jedi Knight.

MAY THE FORCE BE WITH YOU!

PADAWAN PROFILE

NAME

LESLEY SHOLES

BIRTHDAY

2ND OCTOBER

HOME PLANET

EARTH

SPECIES

HUMAN + FAERIE

ALLEGIANCE

JEDI

MODE OF TRANSPORT

FLYING CARPET

LIGHTSABER COLOUR

GREEN

FAVOURITE COMPANIONS

ALI, BRACKEN + MUM

GREATEST STRENGTH

INTUITION

GREATEST WEAKNESS

WORRYING

BIGGEST AMBITION

TO BE A JEDI

QUI-GON JINN

Qui-Gon Jinn was one of the most rebellious Jedi Masters ever to pass through the Temple on Coruscant, but he was also one of the most important. Without him, the Chosen One might never have been discovered . . .

MEMORABLE DATES

92 BBY - Qui-Gon born

82 BBY - Becomes Count Dooku's Padawan

67 BBY - Becomes a Jedi Knight

44 BBY - Takes on a new Padawan, Obi-Wan Kenobi

32 BBY - Meets Anakin Skywalker

32 BBY - Dies by Darth Maul's blade

The kind and enlightened Qui-Gon Jinn believed in living for the moment. He encouraged others to trust their instincts rather than blindly follow the rules. He was greatly respected as a student of the Living Force, despite his maverick reputation.

When he discovered a young slave boy who was strong in the Force, he liberated the child from slavery and took him to Coruscant to be trained as a Jedi. However, the Jedi Council felt that the boy was too old and too full of fear to be successfully trained. Frustrated, Qui-Gon kept the child as his ward, planning to carry out the training himself. That child was Anakin Skywalker.

Before Qui-Gon met Anakin, he had shared many adventures with his Padawan Obi-Wan Kenobi. Together they had journeyed across the galaxy, upholding peace on behalf of the Jedi Order and the Galactic Republic. But as soon as young Skywalker came into their lives, they became part of a chain of events that was guided by the Force.

Qui-Gon was killed by Darth Maul, a Dark Lord of the Sith. His dying wish was that Obi-Wan should train Anakin as a Jedi. Obi-Wan could not refuse such a request, and Anakin's destiny was underway.

GALACTIC STANDARD: BBY / ABY

Galactic civilization has existed for more than 25,000 years. This huge period of time has made it nearly impossible to maintain a standard calendar. Many galactic historians use major events as landmarks instead of dates. At present, the Battle of Yavin is used as a zero point on the calendar. Dates marked **BBY** occurred in years before the Battle of Yavin. Dates marked **ABY** happened in years after the Battle of Yavin.

PALPATINE / DARTH SIDIOUS / THE EMPEROR

Palpatine was a cunning, false and manipulative man, who craved absolute power and was merciless in his pursuit of it. He was a master of deception and a student of the dark side of the Force. Like a crouching, monstrous spider, Palpatine wove his complicated web of treachery over the course of years, with Anakin Skywalker at its centre.

MEMORABLE DATES

82 BBY - Palpatine born
52 BBY - Becomes Senator of Naboo
32 BBY - Battle of Naboo
32 BBY - Elected Supreme Chancellor
22 BBY - Battle of Geonosis
22 BBY - Granted emergency powers by Senate
19 BBY - Declares himself Emperor
0 - Dissolves the Senate
0 - Battle of Yavin
3 ABY - Battle of Hoth
4 ABY - Dies at the hands of Darth Vader

At first, Palpatine was the representative for his home planet of Naboo in the Galactic Senate. However, through his manipulations, Queen Amidala moved for a Vote of No Confidence in Supreme Chancellor Valorum, and Palpatine was elected Supreme Chancellor. No one knew that he was the Sith Lord, Darth Sidious. His strength in the dark side of the Force enabled him to hide the truth from the Galactic Senate and the Jedi Order.

Palpatine's plans were well laid and overwhelming. He would stop at nothing to achieve the power he wanted. Murder, war, death and destruction followed in his wake. While outwardly promising to end corruption, he drowned the Republic in chaos and unrest. He lured Count Dooku to the dark side and manipulated him into creating a Separatist rebellion. His intuition also led him to keep a close eye on Anakin Skywalker. Over the years, he worked hard to make Anakin trust and believe in him. He subtly encouraged Anakin to give way to his fears and passions, thus opening his heart to the dark side. Spurred on by Palpatine's promises of defeating death through the dark side of the Force, Anakin turned his back on the Jedi Order, took the name Darth Vader and became a Dark Lord of the Sith.

Palpatine ruled through tyranny and fear, using his vast clone armies of stormtroopers to crush rebellion. The true horror of his nature was not his evil ambitions, but his intelligence. He knew exactly what he was doing and he knew how many lives were destroyed by his actions. He just didn't care. His death was brought about as a result of Luke Skywalker's strength in the Force. Young Skywalker turned his father away from the Dark Side, and Darth Vader flung Palpatine into the Death Star's reactor core.

THE CHOSEN ONE?

It was the year 32 BBY and the once-peaceful Galactic Republic was in turmoil. The greedy Trade Federation had stopped all shipping to the small planet of Naboo by putting a blockade of starships around the planet. To many this did not seem too serious, but it was the first outward sign of an evil plot that had for decades been bubbling below the surface of galactic politics.

Hoping to avoid a complete breakdown of law and order, Supreme Chancellor Valorum summoned two Jedi Knights, the guardians of peace and justice in the galaxy. He asked them to set out from Coruscant on a secret and delicate mission. Their aim was to settle the conflict and avoid bloodshed. The Jedi that he chose for the mission were two of the most promising in the Jedi Order: Master Qui-Gon Jinn and his Padawan, Obi-Wan Kenobi.

When the Jedi arrived at the blockade, the Viceroy of the Trade Federation, Nute Gunray, was terrified. The reputation of Jedi Knights was formidable. Panicking, Gunray contacted Darth Sidious, a mysterious figure in a hooded cloak that hid his face. Darth Sidious did not seem surprised or worried. In his chilling voice he simply ordered the Viceroy to kill the Jedi Knights.

Droids were sent to do the job, but Jedi are not easy to outwit. Qui-Gon and Obi-Wan evaded the attack and escaped to the planet's surface, but not before they had seen vast numbers of battle droids. They realised at once that this was no ordinary blockade – this was a full-scale invasion. They had to warn Queen Amidala of Naboo.

They stopped on Tatooine to refuel and repair the ship. Qui-Gon took Jar Jar Binks, R2D2 and a handmaiden called Padmé to a nearby settlement to find parts for the ship. What he found instead was the future of the galaxy.

On the planet's surface, Obi-Wan and Qui-Gon met a Gungan called Jar Jar Binks, and together they made the perilous journey to the Naboo capital city. The Trade Federation army had captured the Queen, but the Jedi rescued her and her handmaidens. With the help of a bold and brave droid called R2-D2 they escaped Naboo on a cruiser and set a course for Coruscant. The Queen's only hope now was to persuade the Senate to stop the Trade Federation. When Darth Sidious learned that Queen Amidala had escaped, he sent his Sith apprentice Darth Maul to find her.

En route to Coruscant, the Jedi discovered that the cruiser's hyperdrive had been damaged.

A dealer called Watto had the parts they needed, but they had no money. However, Watto's generous-hearted slave boy Anakin Skywalker offered to enter a Podrace for Qui-Gon. If he won, Qui-Gon would have the money to buy parts for his ship.

Qui-Gon sensed that there was something special about Anakin. The Force was unusually strong with him. When he discovered that the boy's midi-chlorian count was the highest ever known, he made up his mind. If Anakin won the Podrace, he would be taken to Coruscant and be trained as a Jedi.

Meanwhile, Darth Maul had arrived on the planet and sent probe droids across the sandy wasteland, seeking the missing Queen. Time was running out.

Podracing was a dangerous sport – many competitors died during the race, and Padmé and Anakin's mother watched with bated breath. A cheat called Sebulba tried to knock Anakin out of the race, but Anakin's quick reflexes and agility helped him to manoeuvre into first place on the final lap. Sebulba crashed as Anakin whizzed over the finish line to victory.

Thanks to Anakin's triumph, the cruiser was soon repaired. Anakin said goodbye to his mother and the party prepared to leave... but before they could take off, Qui-Gon was attacked by Darth Maul. They fought a fierce lightsaber battle on the sands of Tatooine, until Qui-Gon leaped into the cruiser and escaped, leaving Darth Maul livid.

Senator Palpatine, the Naboo representative in the Senate, met them at Coruscant with bad news. The Senate was filled with greedy, squabbling delegates over whom the Supreme Chancellor had no real power. Palpatine suggested getting a stronger Supreme Chancellor by calling for a Vote of No Confidence in Chancellor Valorum.

The Queen would have done anything to save her people. She followed Palpatine's suggestion and called for a Vote of No Confidence, unwittingly playing into the hands of her enemy. Palpatine was nominated as a candidate for the new Supreme Chancellor and the Queen decided to return to Naboo to be with her people.

In the Jedi Temple, the Council members were reeling from the news that Qui-Gon's attacker was a Sith Lord. As they debated the possibilities behind this, Qui-Gon told them about Anakin. It was his belief that Anakin was the prophesised Chosen One who would bring balance to the Force.

The Council tested Anakin, but they felt that he thought about his mother too much. His fears of losing her were very strong, and fear is the path to the dark side. To Qui-Gon's amazement they refused to train the boy.

Qui-Gon vowed to train Anakin himself, but before anything else could be decided, they all had to return to Naboo with the Queen. It was vital to discover the identity of the Sith warrior.

When they returned to Naboo, they went straight to see Boss Nass, the Gungan leader. The Queen prepared to speak, but suddenly her handmaiden Padmé stepped forward. To the astonishment of everyone except wise Qui-Gon, she revealed that she was really Queen Amidala. She had been using a decoy to fool her enemies, but now the time had come to reveal her true identity and beg Boss Nass for his help.

Padmé and Boss Nass drew up battle plans. The Gungans would draw the droid army away from the capital city with a decoy battle. At the same time, Padmé would lead a strike team into the city and capture the Viceroy. They would also send pilots into space to destroy the droid control ship that was orbiting the planet. Without the control ship, the battle droids on the planet's surface would be useless.

The plan worked smoothly at first. The Gungans marched on the droid army as Padmé and her team crept into the city. As the brave Naboo pilots took off in their starfighters, Anakin and R2-D2 hid in the cockpit of a spare fighter.

The team's presence was detected and a fight broke out in the hangar between the Naboo and the droids. Darth Maul appeared, wielding a cruel-looking double-bladed lightsaber. His red eyes glowed with hatred as he launched himself at Qui-Gon and Obi-Wan.

While the Jedi were occupied with Darth Maul, Anakin turned his starfighter's weapons on the droids. He shot them down, enabling Padmé to escape with her team. So far so good... but Anakin's fighter was now on automatic pilot, and he had no idea how to stop it. The craft zoomed up into space to join the battle against the droid control ship, carrying Anakin with it.

Padmé and her team captured the Viceroy, but the Gungans were losing their battle against the Trade Federation's gargantuan droid army. They were fighting well, but they were hopelessly outnumbered. However, help was at hand. In the skies above, R2-D2 had managed to get the starfighter out of autopilot and Anakin flew into the droid control ship. He shot at the main reactor and only just escaped as it exploded into tiny pieces. Without their control vessel, all the droids on Naboo stopped working and the Gungans were safe!

Meanwhile, the battle was still in full flow between Darth Maul, Qui-Gon and Obi-Wan. The Sith apprentice led the Jedi onto a narrow bridge, jumping and twisting as he attacked. He threw Obi-Wan off the bridge and continued to fight Qui-Gon. It was a mighty duel, but Darth Maul was young and fast – at last, with a leer of triumph, he plunged his lightsaber into Qui-Gon's stomach. The older Jedi dropped like a stone.

Obi-Wan pulled himself up and rushed towards Darth Maul. Obi-Wan was a powerful fighter, young, athletic and fast. At last, after a mighty and vicious battle, he managed to cut the evil Sith in half with his lightsaber.

His heart hammering with care and concern, Obi-Wan rushed to his Master's side. One glance showed that it was too late to save him. With his last breath, Qui-Gon made Obi-Wan promise to train Anakin as a Jedi. Obi-Wan agreed and his Master died in his arms. Obi-Wan would never be the same again.

Palpatine was elected Supreme Chancellor and promised to bring peace and prosperity to the Republic. Obi-Wan was made a Jedi Knight and the Jedi Council agreed to let Anakin be his Padawan learner. It seemed as if the dark times had come and gone. But the wisest of the Jedi knew that this was not the case.

At Qui-Gon's funeral, Mace Windu and Yoda shared their feelings of imbalance and alarm. It was bad enough that the Sith had risen again, but the death of Darth Maul was not the end. Yoda and Mace knew that there was always two Sith – a Master and an apprentice. The apprentice had been destroyed, but who – and *where* – was the Master?

PADAWAN CHALLENGE:
ODD ONE OUT

Bounty Hunter

LOOK AT THESE FOUR FACES. NAME THEM AND
SEARCH YOUR THOUGHTS FOR EVERY FACT YOU
KNOW ABOUT THEM. CAN YOU WORK OUT WHICH
IS THE ODD ONE OUT... AND *WHY*?

Anakin Skywalker

Darth Sideous

HINT: WHICH GIFTED WARRIOR HAS BATTLED THREE OF THESE FOUR PEOPLE?

18

R2-D2 HAS BEEN PROGRAMMED WITH A SERIES OF CODED MESSAGES THAT ARE VITAL TO THE SUCCESS OF THE REBELLION. HOWEVER, THE CODE BREAKER HAS BEEN LOST AND THE REBEL ALLIANCE IS RUNNING OUT OF TIME. EXAMINE THEM CAREFULLY. CAN YOU CRACK THE CODES AND SAVE THE LIVES OF COUNTLESS REBEL SOLDIERS?

UMT FTITYH QAYY FTZJTGSXCH KU 0800 MXCFH KU UMT XCUTF FAE.

_EE/___ R_/__ RR/_ G____ D__/ __/0800/ED___/__/_ E_/D____/__ T

YCPT HPRQKYPTF QAYY YTKJ UMT HVCKJFXZ.

R___/___ R___/_ RR/ R___/_E_/_____ DG

BFAZNTHH YTAK AH NKFFRAZO UMT BYKZH XL UMT JTKUM HUKF.

___G_____/R___/__/_____G_/_E_/_R_G_D_/_E_/____E/_____

A	B	C	D	E	F	G	H	I	J	K	L	M
		T									Y	E

N	O	P	Q	R	S	T	U	V	W	X	Y	Z
										D	R	G

PADAWAN CHALLENGE:

CODE BREAKER

GALAXY QUIZ

HOW GOOD IS YOUR MEMORY? CAN YOU ALWAYS PUT A NAME TO A FACE? HOW ABOUT A SPECIES? STUDY THESE FACES AND THEN FILL OUT THE NAME AND SPECIES OF EACH ONE. GOOD LUCK!

NAME: CHEWBACCA
SPECIES: WOOKIE

NAME: JAR JAR BINKS
SPECIES: GUNGAN

NAME: JABBA THE HUT
SPECIES:

NAME:
SPECIES:

NAME:
SPECIES:

NAME: WATTO
SPECIES:

NAME:
SPECIES:

NAME:
SPECIES: WOOKIE

NAME:
SPECIES:

NAME:
SPECIES:

CHECK YOUR ANSWERS ON PAGE 110/111 AND ADD UP YOUR SCORE.
(YOU WILL ALWAYS GET ONE POINT FOR EVERY CORRECT ANSWER.)

TOTAL SCORE FOR GALAXY QUIZ PART 1

OBI-WAN KENOBI

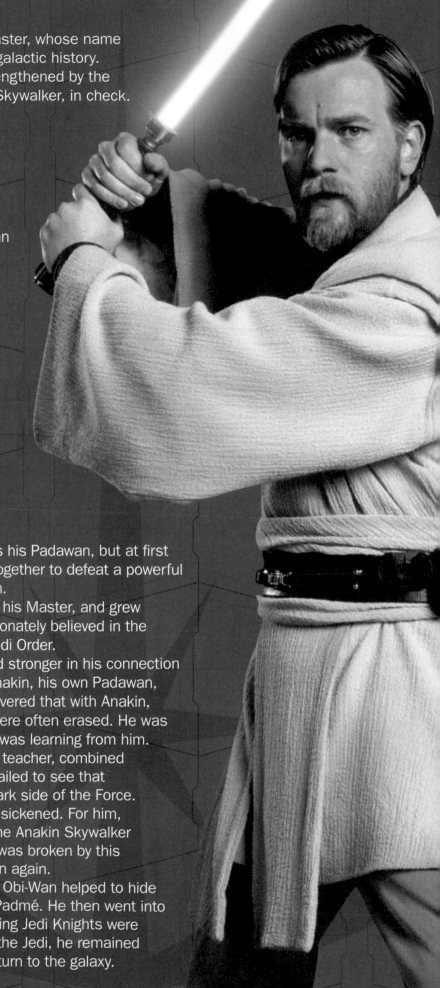

O bi-Wan Kenobi was a brave and wise Jedi Master, whose name
will be remembered forever in the annals of galactic history.
His sense of caution and discipline were strengthened by the
need to keep his wild spirited Padawan, Anakin Skywalker, in check.

MEMORABLE DATES

57 BBY - Obi-Wan Kenobi born

44 BBY - Becomes Padawan to Qui-Gon Jinn

32 BBY - Becomes a Jedi Knight

32 BBY - Takes Anakin Skywalker as his Padawan

22 BBY - Discovers clone army being
created on Kamino

19 BBY - Defeats General Grievous on Utapau

19 BBY - Duels with Anakin on Mustafar

19 BBY - Delivers Luke Skywalker to the Lars
family on Tatooine

0 - Introduces Luke Skywalker to the Force

0 - Becomes one with the Force during
a duel with Darth Vader

Obi-Wan began his Jedi training when he was
brought to the Jedi Temple at a very young age.
He was a hard-working, careful pupil, but by the
time he turned thirteen he had still not been
accepted as a Jedi's Padawan.

Yoda hoped that Qui-Gon would take Obi-Wan as his Padawan, but at first
Qui-Gon refused. However, the Force drew them together to defeat a powerful
enemy and Qui-Gon finally agreed to train Obi-Wan.

Obi-Wan learned much wisdom and insight from his Master, and grew
to be a thoughtful and fiercely loyal Jedi. He passionately believed in the
Force's power for good and in the beliefs of the Jedi Order.

As the years passed, Obi-Wan grew stronger and stronger in his connection
with the Living Force. However, his affection for Anakin, his own Padawan,
made him blind to certain dangers. Obi-Wan discovered that with Anakin,
the boundaries between Master and apprentice were often erased. He was
learning from the boy almost as much as the boy was learning from him.
But because of Obi-Wan's lack of experience as a teacher, combined
with his proud refusal to seek help or advice, he failed to see that
Anakin was being lured closer and closer to the dark side of the Force.

When Anakin became Darth Vader, Obi-Wan felt sickened. For him,
it was as if Darth Vader was a different person. The Anakin Skywalker
he had known was dead forever. Obi-Wan's heart was broken by this
betrayal, and he too would never be the same man again.

Amid the chaos surrounding the rise of the Sith, Obi-Wan helped to hide
the twin son and daughter born to Anakin's wife, Padmé. He then went into
hiding as the Empire rose and most of the remaining Jedi Knights were
slaughtered. Although he brooded over the fall of the Jedi, he remained
hopeful that one day, somehow, balance would return to the galaxy.

COUNT DOOKU

Count Dooku was once a highly respected Jedi who had been trained by Yoda himself. However, a dark seed of pride and disdain had lurked inside his heart. Eventually his private thoughts became public knowledge, for he abandoned the Jedi Order and transferred his loyalties to the dark side and the mysterious Sith Lord, Darth Sidious. Through Count Dooku, Darth Sidious would start a war that would split the galaxy itself apart.

MEMORABLE DATES

102 BBY - Count Dooku born

89 BBY - Chosen as a Padawan

82 BBY - Becomes a Jedi Knight

67 BBY - Becomes a Jedi Master

32 BBY - Leaves the Jedi Order and goes into exile

31.5 BBY - Hires Jango Fett

24 BBY - Becomes leader of the Separatists

22 BBY - Battle of Geonosis

19 BBY - Dies by Anakin Skywalker's hand

Dooku's strong-minded views challenged and sometimes defied the Jedi Council. He studied the ways of the Force for almost eighty years, but he remained most closely attached to his pride, intuitions and ideals. His strong sense of independence was a cause of concern, but despite his stubbornness he was a formidable Jedi.

As one of the wealthiest men in the galaxy, Dooku could have afforded an army on his own fortune alone. His strength in the Force made him hard to read, and therefore his overwhelming interest in power was underestimated.

Because of his political idealism Dooku desired a separation between the Jedi and the corrupt Republic. He believed that the Jedi would only weaken by serving such a rotten institution. In the end, he could bear it no longer and he left the Order.

Behind his elegant manners and seductive charisma, Dooku was little more than a pawn of the Sith. By Sith tradition, Dooku took on a new name – Darth Tyranus – and began a campaign of unrest that would lead to the death of the Republic. The once-respected Jedi Master stirred up feelings of discontent and encouraged thousands of star systems to follow his example and join the growing Separatist movement.

MACE WINDU

Mace Windu was a senior member of the Jedi Council, who was almost as respected as Yoda. He was a man of deep wisdom and legendary achievements. Despite his calm and peaceful nature, Mace was the most fearsome warrior on the Jedi Council.

MEMORABLE DATES

72 BBY - Mace Windu born

58 BBY - Builds lightsaber

50 BBY - Joins Jedi Council

22 BBY - Battle of Geonosis

19 BBY - Dies fighting Palpatine

Mace Windu's skills and accomplishments in battle were partly due to his ability to remain calm in the face of danger and death. He had complete mastery over Jedi fighting styles, and was willing to place himself in peril for the sake of any just cause.

Mace Windu appeared to lead by firm example, following established rules and discipline. Despite this, he was also one of the quickest of the Jedi to appreciate a joke, and would often spring philosophical traps during debates. In battle, he seemed almost impossible to defeat, because his moves were so fluid and unexpected. His creative flair gave an edge to his intellectual abilities, forming a character that was multi-layered and difficult to analyse.

Mace was always wary of Anakin Skywalker, and had initially opposed allowing him to train as a Jedi. He did not know whether or not young Skywalker was really the Chosen One, but he felt an instinctive distrust of him that it was impossible to shake off. His concerns were proved sadly justified when he went to arrest Palpatine. Rather than allow the Sith Lord to be removed from power, Anakin cut off Mace's hand, enabling Palpatine to destroy him. One of the greatest Jedi of all time was the first casualty of Anakin's fall to the dark side.

DRAMATIC DISCOVERIES

Ten years after the Trade Federation's attack on Naboo, there was great unrest in the Galactic Senate. The rogue Jedi Count Dooku had persuaded several thousand solar systems to leave the Republic, and it seemed as if the Republic was crumbling. It was becoming increasingly difficult for the Jedi to maintain peace and order in the galaxy, and some Senators wanted to create their own army. However, the Jedi did not believe that preparing for war was the right way to maintain peace and persuade the Separatists to return.

Padmé Amidala, the former Queen of Naboo, was now a Senator. Her passionate belief in peace made her fiercely opposed to the new idea of creating an army of the Republic. This outspoken opposition had led to an attempt on her life, so she was placed under the protection of Master Obi-Wan Kenobi and his Padawan learner, Anakin Skywalker. Obi-Wan and Anakin met Padmé again for the first time in ten years.

As a child, Anakin had thought that Padmé was as beautiful as an angel. Now he could not keep his eyes off her. However, to his confusion and frustration, it soon became clear that Padmé still thought of him as a little boy.

Obi-Wan and Anakin stood guard outside Padmé's bedroom as she slept, but even their acute senses did not realise the danger until it was almost too late. A hired assassin called Zam Wesell put poisonous kouhuns into the Senator's room. Just in time, the Jedi sensed danger and rushed in. Anakin killed the creatures and then he and Obi-Wan chased Zam through the busy streets of Coruscant.

The Jedi finally caught up with their quarry in a club. Realising that she had been caught fair and square, Zam was about to tell them the name of the bounty hunter who had hired her. But as she opened her mouth to speak, a toxic dart flew through the air and killed her instantaneously.

The Jedi were just in time to see her helmeted killer fly away with a rocket pack on his back.

Obi-Wan was ordered to track down the bounty hunter, so it was left to Anakin to escort Padmé safely back to Naboo. As they travelled, he talked freely about being a Jedi and his frustrated sense that Obi-Wan was holding him back. Padmé began to realise that Anakin was no longer a child.

Obi-Wan discovered that the toxic dart that killed Zam came from Kamino, a planet of skilled cloners beyond the Outer Rim. However, this led to a worrying discovery. The Jedi Archive charts for Kamino had been erased from the Archive's memory. It was as if the planet did not exist . . . and worst of all, only a Jedi could erase the files.

Obi-Wan flew to Kamino and was taken to meet the Prime Minister, Lama Su, who seemed to be expecting him. Obi-Wan's concern mounted as he learned that for years, the Kaminoans had been developing a vast clone army for the Republic. As he examined the hundreds of thousands of clone troopers, he learned that the original host was a bounty hunter called Jango Fett.

Apart from his pay, Jango had demanded an unaltered clone for himself, which he was bringing up as his son. Obi-Wan suspected at once that Jango was the bounty hunter who had been trying to kill Senator Amidala – although he could not imagine why he would.

On Naboo, Padmé and Anakin were growing closer and closer. Before they fully realised it themselves, they had fallen deeply in love. Anakin longed for love and affection, but Padmé managed to stay practical. The Jedi were not allowed to marry, so their love could never be. She told Anakin that she could not live a lie.

That night, Anakin had a terrible nightmare about his mother, Shmi. Certain that she was in danger, he decided to return to his home planet of Tatooine, disobeying the Jedi Council's orders to remain on Naboo. Padmé went with him, worried for his feelings, and they set off in a cruiser with R2-D2.

Obi-Wan sent a report to Yoda and Mace Windu, who ordered him to bring Jango Fett in for questioning. However, Jango and his son escaped, and Obi-Wan was forced to pursue them across the stars to a planet called Geonosis. Count Dooku was there with Nute Gunray, the Viceroy of the Trade Federation. They had created a huge army of battle droids to overwhelm the Jedi and get the Republic to submit to their demands. Obi-Wan tried to transmit a message to Anakin, but he was seen by a Geonosian and captured. He could only hope that his message had reached Anakin in time.

On Tatooine, Anakin and Padmé discovered that Shmi had been sold to a moisture farmer called Cliegg Lars, who freed her and married her. But when they found the Lars farm, a terrible and devastating discovery awaited them. Shmi had been captured by the notoriously cruel Tusken Raiders.

Anakin reached the Tusken Raiders' camp too late. His mother had been tortured and beaten, and she died in her son's arms. Anakin was overcome by anger and grief. He turned on the Tusken Raiders with his lightsaber and pitilessly slew them all. He had opened his heart and let rage and hatred enter. He would never be free of those emotions again.

Anakin returned to Padmé to find Obi-Wan's message. Against his orders, Anakin set off to Geonosis with Padmé by his side. He could not abandon his Master.

Back on Coruscant, the Senate granted Palpatine emergency powers so that he could make instant decisions about this latest threat to the Republic. He now had complete control, but he promised that he would give up his new power when the crisis was over. He went on to announce his first decision as acting dictator – the Republic would use the clone army to fight the Separatists.

When Padmé and Anakin arrived on Geonosis they were captured and condemned to death. Sure that they were about to die, Padmé felt that she had nothing left to lose. She told Anakin that she loved him. Now she had admitted it, there could be no turning back. They were led into the execution arena with Obi-Wan. Dooku, Jango Fett and the Separatist leaders looked on as three ravening beasts were pushed into the arena.

To the astonishment of the onlookers, Padmé, Obi-Wan and Anakin fought and overpowered the beasts. The Geonosians were furious to have been deprived of the grisly scene. Droidekas rolled into the arena, ready to gun down the three prisoners. However, before the order to kill could be given, a cloaked figure held a lightsaber to Jango Fett's throat. It was Mace Windu.

Support had arrived at last. All around the arena, Jedi Knights pulled off their cloaks and ignited their lightsabers. It was a terrifying sight for the Geonosians and the cowardly Separatist leaders. Only Dooku seemed unafraid. He called his droids into the arena and an almighty battle began.

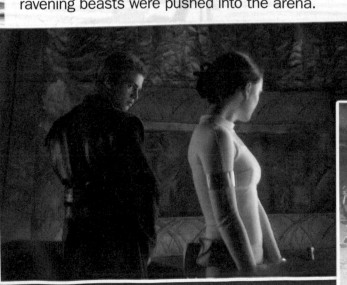

As the Jedi fought to protect each other and Mace cut off Jango Fett's head, Yoda swept out of the sky with a fleet of gunships and clone troopers. Soon the droid army was in full retreat. Count Dooku set off on a speeder, planning to escape to his Master, Darth Sidious.

Obi-Wan and Anakin followed Count Dooku and tried to defeat him in combat, but Dooku was a master warrior. He knocked Obi-Wan out and cut off Anakin's arm. But before Dooku could gloat or turn to leave, there was a noise behind him. It was Yoda.

Dooku and Yoda duelled so fast that they were little more than blurs. But Count Dooku could not defeat his old Master, and cheating was the only option left to him. He used the Force to attack the defenceless Obi-Wan and Anakin. While Yoda was protecting them, Dooku made his escape.

There were many results of these events, both large and small. On a personal level, Anakin got a new mechanical arm and married Padmé in secret. On a galactic level, Supreme Chancellor Palpatine gave orders for thousands of clone troopers and watched them march into battle ships, ready for war. But these seemingly unconnected events would one day erupt in the faces of everyone concerned.

Yoda was grim and worried. He knew that one of the darkest times in galactic history had begun. He would have been even more alarmed if he had known that everything was moving along according to Darth Sidious's evil plan...

A GRIEVOUS CHALLENGE

FOLLOW THESE SIMPLE STEPS
TO BECOME A JEDI ARTIST AND
CREATE YOUR OWN PICTURE OF
THE DREADED GENERAL GRIEVOUS!

CLONE CROSSWORD

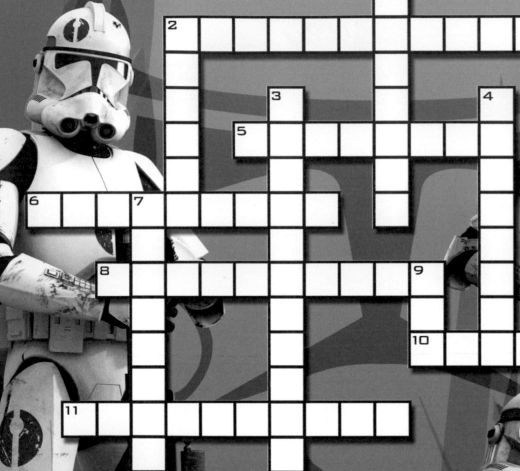

ACROSS

2. Order 66 instructed the clones to _____ ___ ____.
5. Where was the Chosen One found?
6. Who were the clone soldiers created from?
8. What is a Jedi's weapon?
10. On which planet did Darth Vader destroy the Separatist Council?
11. What was Darth Tyranus's other name?

DOWN

1. Who is this Jedi? (See image right)
2. On which planet were the clone soldiers grown?
3. Which Sith Lord was planning the Clone Wars for decades?
4. Which battle began the Clone Wars?
7. Which Clone Wars general collected the weapons of Jedi he killed?
9. Tatooine is a planet in the Outer ___.

SONEOGIS

BONAO

MOIKAN

USCCORTAN

How's your intergalactic geography? The names of these planets have become scrambled in the Jedi archives. Use your knowledge and your strength in the Force to decipher each planet's true name.

ATINETOO

OHHT

REDON

VINAY

WORD SCRAMBLE

GALAXY QUIZ

How much do you know about the lives of Obi-Wan Kenobi, Anakin Skywalker and the other heroes of the golden era? Complete this quiz and find out!

1. Name this rebellious Jedi.

2. Who introduced Qui-Gon and Obi-Wan to Boss Nass?

3. Who was Darth Sidious's first apprentice?

4. On which planet did Qui-Gon lose his life?

5. Name this weapon of war.

6. Who owned Anakin Skywalker when he was a slave?

7. What did Qui-Gon discover about Anakin Skywalker's blood?

8. Who did Jango Fett hire to assassinate Padmé Amidala?

9. How many beasts did the Geonosians set on Obi-Wan, Anakin and Padmé?

11. Name this enemy of the Republic.

12. Who did Obi-Wan fight on Mustafar?

13. Who kidnapped Chancellor Palpatine?

14. Who killed Shmi Skywalker?

10. Name this enemy of Anakin Skywalker.

15. Who was adopted by Bail Organa

CHECK YOUR ANSWERS ON PAGE 110/111 AND ADD UP YOUR SCORE. (YOU WILL ALWAYS GET ONE POINT FOR EVERY CORRECT ANSWER.)

TOTAL SCORE FOR GALAXY QUIZ PART 2

PADMÉ AMIDALA

Intelligent and fiercely loyal, Padmé Amidala was one of the most celebrated of the Naboo. By a young age she had already served as Queen and become a Senator for her planet. Her courage, honesty and kindness made her a respected and trusted member of the Senate, but her secret marriage to Anakin Skywalker would lead ultimately to ruin and despair.

MEMORABLE DATES

46 BBY - Padmé Naberrie born

35 BBY - Becomes an Apprentice Legislator

34 BBY - Becomes Princess of Theed

32.5 BBY - Elected Queen of Naboo and gets the name Amidala

32 BBY - Battle of Naboo

32 BBY - Meets Anakin Skywalker

24.5 BBY - Becomes Senator

22 BBY - Marries Anakin Skywalker

22 BBY - Battle of Geonosis

19 BBY - Gives birth to twins, Luke and Leia

19 BBY - Dies after Anakin Skywalker breaks her heart

Padmé was born in a small village on Naboo, but even from these humble beginnings she stood out as one of Naboo's brightest children. From her earliest years her greatest ambition was to serve her home planet and its people. She was the supervisor of the city of Theed for two years before being elected Queen of Naboo. She replaced King Veruna, who abandoned the throne in the midst of scandal. Padme was chosen in an electronic global election that lasted less than four minutes.

After her term as Queen ended, she became a Senator and worked tirelessly to achieve peace and stability in the galaxy. She was a determined and visionary politician.

By the time she met Anakin Skywalker again, Padmé had grown into a young woman with powerful self-discipline and a practical nature. However, Anakin awoke feelings in her heart that she could not seem to control, however hard she tried.

Due to her passionate political interests and her secret love for Anakin Skywalker, Padmé was at the very heart of the events that led to the downfall of the Jedi. It was she, spurred on by Palpatine, who called for a Vote of No Confidence in Supreme Chancellor Valorum. This enabled Palpatine to become Supreme Chancellor.

Padmé's strength and determination were so powerful that they carried her through her secret marriage and her political career. However, in the end her love for Anakin destroyed her. Realising that he had turned to the dark side broke her heart, and without his love to live for, she faded away.

The name of Padmé Amidala will forever represent faith, love and hope in the face of despair. Even in her darkest hour, she believed that Anakin could be saved. She died believing that there was still good in him, and twenty-three years later, her son Luke would prove her right.

GENERAL GRIEVOUS

General Grievous was a creature seemingly born for war. Even his body was a deadly weapon, and his name struck fear into the hearts of some of the bravest Jedi. He became Supreme Commander of the Confederacy, and in this position his sadistic ambitions knew no limits.

MEMORABLE DATES

28 BBY - Becomes a cyborg
19 BBY - Battle of Coruscant

General Grievous was the face of the enemy, and his fearsome reputation terrified the Republic. To many, he was more frightening than Count Dooku. He was known as a merciless military leader. This was reinforced by his personal fleet of specialised killing machines and vehicles.

Grievous hunted Jedi for sport, and he had many lightsabers, which he kept as trophies. He carried his four favourites with him at all times, because they reminded him of the Jedi he murdered. Touching these souvenirs made him feel something like happiness.

The General's body was a weapon made of metal and flesh. His unique fighting form and mechanical body gave him an extra edge in close-quarters combat, and his strategic genius and matchless intelligence made him almost unbeatable. In one memorable battle, Grievous fought four Jedi at once and killed them.

Grievous was trained in lightsaber combat by Count Dooku. At the start of the Clone Wars, Dooku pitted his apprentices Asajj Ventress and Durge against Grievous and proved that Grievous was able to lead the droid army. The General eventually died in combat, but his legacy lasted throughout the years, and his name will forever be synonymous with fear, cruelty and hatred.

ANAKIN SKYWALKER

A nakin Skywalker was exceptionally strong in the Force, and many thought that the Force had created him, for he was also known as the Chosen One. However, no one could have guessed what that truly meant. Anakin was destined to suffer crippling loss and anguished mental torments before he could finally be at peace.

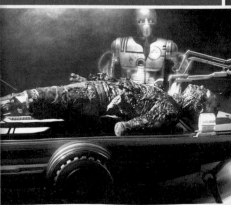

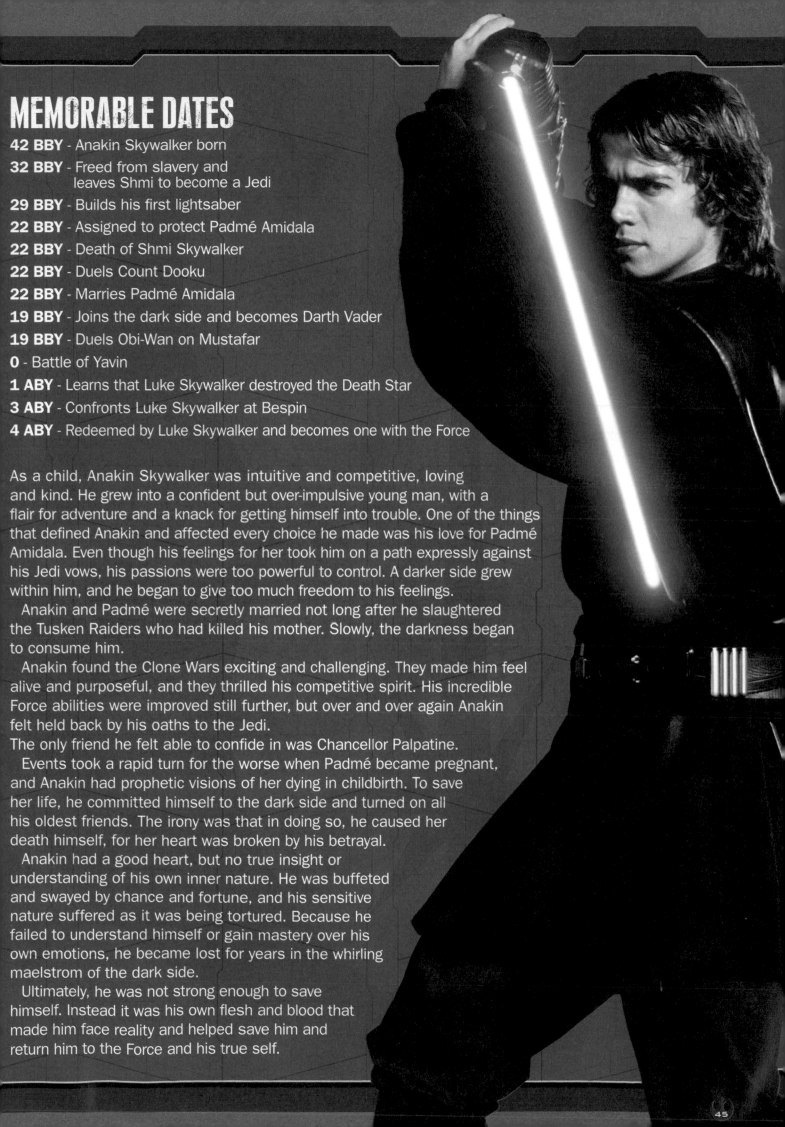

MEMORABLE DATES

42 BBY - Anakin Skywalker born

32 BBY - Freed from slavery and leaves Shmi to become a Jedi

29 BBY - Builds his first lightsaber

22 BBY - Assigned to protect Padmé Amidala

22 BBY - Death of Shmi Skywalker

22 BBY - Duels Count Dooku

22 BBY - Marries Padmé Amidala

19 BBY - Joins the dark side and becomes Darth Vader

19 BBY - Duels Obi-Wan on Mustafar

0 - Battle of Yavin

1 ABY - Learns that Luke Skywalker destroyed the Death Star

3 ABY - Confronts Luke Skywalker at Bespin

4 ABY - Redeemed by Luke Skywalker and becomes one with the Force

As a child, Anakin Skywalker was intuitive and competitive, loving and kind. He grew into a confident but over-impulsive young man, with a flair for adventure and a knack for getting himself into trouble. One of the things that defined Anakin and affected every choice he made was his love for Padmé Amidala. Even though his feelings for her took him on a path expressly against his Jedi vows, his passions were too powerful to control. A darker side grew within him, and he began to give too much freedom to his feelings.

Anakin and Padmé were secretly married not long after he slaughtered the Tusken Raiders who had killed his mother. Slowly, the darkness began to consume him.

Anakin found the Clone Wars exciting and challenging. They made him feel alive and purposeful, and they thrilled his competitive spirit. His incredible Force abilities were improved still further, but over and over again Anakin felt held back by his oaths to the Jedi.
The only friend he felt able to confide in was Chancellor Palpatine.

Events took a rapid turn for the worse when Padmé became pregnant, and Anakin had prophetic visions of her dying in childbirth. To save her life, he committed himself to the dark side and turned on all his oldest friends. The irony was that in doing so, he caused her death himself, for her heart was broken by his betrayal.

Anakin had a good heart, but no true insight or understanding of his own inner nature. He was buffeted and swayed by chance and fortune, and his sensitive nature suffered as it was being tortured. Because he failed to understand himself or gain mastery over his own emotions, he became lost for years in the whirling maelstrom of the dark side.

Ultimately, he was not strong enough to save himself. Instead it was his own flesh and blood that made him face reality and helped save him and return him to the Force and his true self.

THE TERROR

Since the Battle of Geonosis three years earlier, the Clone Wars had raged across the galaxy. Supreme Chancellor Palpatine had gained enough support from the Senate to have almost absolute power, and the Senate had grown increasingly corrupt. Now the fiendish droid leader General Grievous had kidnapped Chancellor Palpatine, and Obi-Wan and Anakin were leading a desperate mission to rescue him.

In near space above the planet's surface, General Grievous's ship was waiting for them. The Jedi dodged incoming laser fire, vulture droid fighters and droid tri-fighters, and fought their way on board the ship.

After fighting battle droids, Obi-Wan and Anakin found Palpatine shackled to a chair. Before they could rescue him, Count Dooku strode into the room and engaged the two Jedi in battle.

Obi-Wan was defeated and knocked out, but Anakin was no longer a young Padawan. He cut off Count Dooku's hands and Dooku stumbled to the floor. Palpatine urged Anakin to kill him, and the young man's blood was racing through his veins with excitement. Against the Jedi code, Anakin cut off Count Dooku's head.

After a battle with General Grievous and a crash landing, the Jedi returned the Chancellor to Coruscant. While the Jedi Council greeted the Chancellor, Anakin sought out his wife. Their marriage was still a secret, but it could not remain so for much longer, for now Padmé told him that she was pregnant. She was worried that he would be expelled from the Order, but he was so happy to see her and to hear the news that nothing could upset him.

However, Anakin's happiness was short-lived, for he began to suffer from prophetic nightmares that Padmé would die in childbirth. He was so afraid of losing her that he was prepared to do anything to save her life. He could not accept that death is a natural part of life.

Palpatine had spent years nurturing Anakin's trust and friendship, and it now began to pay off. The Jedi were beginning to feel suspicious of the Chancellor, so Palpatine appointed Anakin as his representative on the Jedi Council. He wanted Anakin to be the eyes, ears and voice of the Republic. Anakin was thrilled by the honour, but though the Council accepted him as a member, it refused to accept him as a Master. Anakin lost his temper and began to feel more and more strongly that the Council were unfair to Palpatine.

When the Council asked him to spy on the Chancellor he was upset and confused. He told Palpatine this, and the Chancellor was happy to hear it. His plans to turn the 'Chosen One' to the dark side were advancing steadily. He even dared to tell Anakin a little about the Sith, and revealed that they had discovered how to stop death itself. In light of his nightmares, Anakin was very interested to hear this.

Obi-Wan left to find General Grievous, little guessing that this would be the last time he would see the Anakin Skywalker he knew. He located Grievous on Utapau, and after a long and deadly battle, he succeeded in destroying the cruel general.

When Palpatine heard that Grievous has been found, he felt that the time was right to reveal the truth to Anakin. He told the young Jedi that he alone could teach him the ways of the dark side and help him save Padmé's life. Anakin could not believe what he was hearing. His mentor was a Sith Lord! But even as he showed his disgust and horror, Palpatine continued to bombard him with doubt.

Anakin told the Jedi Council that Palpatine was a Sith, and Mace went to arrest him. However, Palpatine fought back and battled Mace fiercely. As they duelled, Anakin realised that if Palpatine died, he would lose all chance of saving Padmé. At last he rushed to the Chancellor's chambers and arrived just in time to see Mace knock Palpatine's lightsaber out of his hand.

The Jedi pushed Palpatine right to the edge of the ledge, and Palpatine attacked Mace with bolts of Sith lightning, which began to arch back towards the Sith Lord. His face twisted and distorted, and his eyes became yellow as he struggled to intensify his powers.

The Chancellor begged for his life, but Mace felt that he was too dangerous to be kept alive. Unable to bear the thought of losing Padmé forever, Anakin lunged forward and cut off Mace's lightsaber hand as he was about to strike down Palpatine. As Mace stared at him in shock, the Sith Lord sprang to life and bombarded the Jedi Master with powerful bolts of Sith lightning. Mace was flung out of the window and fell to his death.

Palpatine cackled with delight, his face a terrible mask of evil. Anakin was horrified. But Palpatine encouraged the young Jedi to fulfil his destiny and become his apprentice – to learn to use the dark side of the Force.

Anakin paused, but then thought of Padmé and knew that he would do anything to save her. He knelt before Palpatine and pledged himself to his teachings and the ways of the Sith. From now on he would be known as Darth Vader.

The Jedi were declared enemies of the Republic, and Palpatine sent Anakin to the Jedi Temple to destroy all the Jedi there, telling his new apprentice to show no mercy. From there, Anakin was commissioned to travel to the Mustafar system and wipe out Nute Gunray and the other Separatist leaders. Finally Palpatine was able to instruct his clone commanders to carry out Order 66: Kill all Jedi.

With a terrible suspicion clutching at his heart, Obi-Wan used a control panel to activate the stored security hologram. The image showed Anakin slaughtering Jedi, both young and old. Obi-Wan and Yoda looked on in horror as they watched Anakin kneel before the dark-robed figure of Lord Sidious. Tears began to well up in Obi-Wan's eyes and he turned away from the grisly scene. They knew that the boy Obi-Wan had trained was gone forever – consumed by Darth Vader. Yoda left to face Lord Sidious, and Obi-Wan to find his former Padawan... and kill him.

Anakin arrived on Mustafar and cut the Separatist leaders down one by one. At the end of the destruction, his face had transformed. Like his Master, Lord Sidious, his eyes glowed yellow.

In the Senate Chamber, Palpatine addressed the crowd. He stated that the Republic would be reorganised into the first Galactic Empire, for a safe and secure society that would last for ten thousand years. The Empire would be controlled by a sovereign ruler, who would be chosen for life, and a new constitution would be formed. Padmé was devastated. Liberty was dying amid thunderous applause.

Across the galaxy, Jedi fell in their hundreds as the clones turned on them. A few survived, such as Yoda and Obi-Wan, but most others were not so lucky. Yoda and Obi-Wan met Senator Bail Organa aboard the *Tantive IV* to decide their next course of action.

Anakin visited Padmé and told her that the Jedi had turned on the Republic, and were now traitors. He informed her that he was going to Mustafar, and begged her to trust him and wait for him.

Palpatine had sent out a coded message to all Jedi ordering them to return to the Temple. When Yoda and Obi-Wan discovered this, they immediately set out to dismantle the coded signal – it was obviously a trap. They succeeded in turning it off, but in the Temple they found many bodies of young students, and realised that they had been killed by a lightsaber.

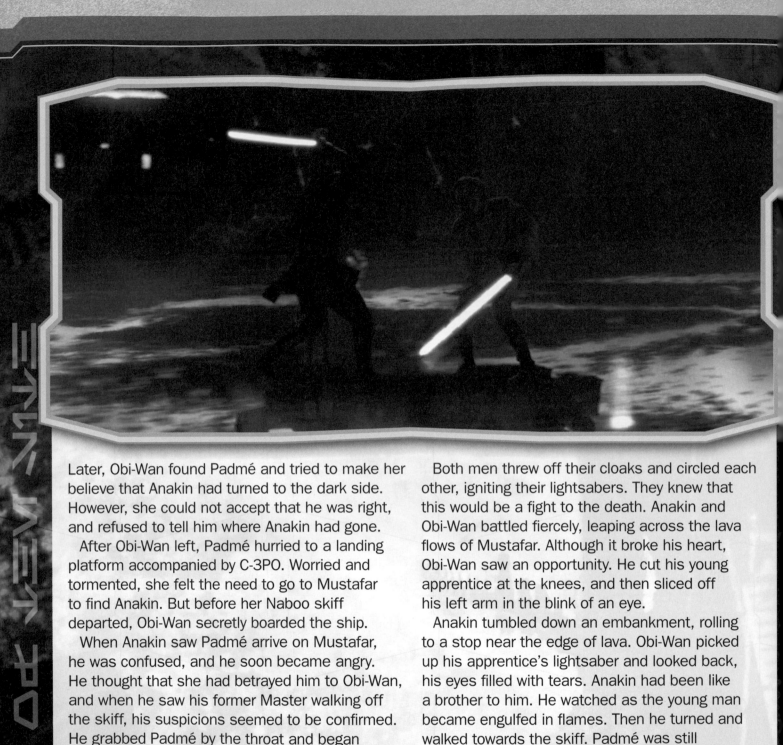

Later, Obi-Wan found Padmé and tried to make her believe that Anakin had turned to the dark side. However, she could not accept that he was right, and refused to tell him where Anakin had gone.

After Obi-Wan left, Padmé hurried to a landing platform accompanied by C-3PO. Worried and tormented, she felt the need to go to Mustafar to find Anakin. But before her Naboo skiff departed, Obi-Wan secretly boarded the ship.

When Anakin saw Padmé arrive on Mustafar, he was confused, and he soon became angry. He thought that she had betrayed him to Obi-Wan, and when he saw his former Master walking off the skiff, his suspicions seemed to be confirmed. He grabbed Padmé by the throat and began to choke her. Obi-Wan begged Anakin to let her go, and as he released his grip Padmé sank to the ground.

Both men threw off their cloaks and circled each other, igniting their lightsabers. They knew that this would be a fight to the death. Anakin and Obi-Wan battled fiercely, leaping across the lava flows of Mustafar. Although it broke his heart, Obi-Wan saw an opportunity. He cut his young apprentice at the knees, and then sliced off his left arm in the blink of an eye.

Anakin tumbled down an embankment, rolling to a stop near the edge of lava. Obi-Wan picked up his apprentice's lightsaber and looked back, his eyes filled with tears. Anakin had been like a brother to him. He watched as the young man became engulfed in flames. Then he turned and walked towards the skiff. Padmé was still unconscious, and she needed medical attention.

Master Yoda entered the Chancellor's office and prepared to do battle. He knew that if he could not defeat Palpatine now, the galaxy was in grave danger. Everything depended on his success.

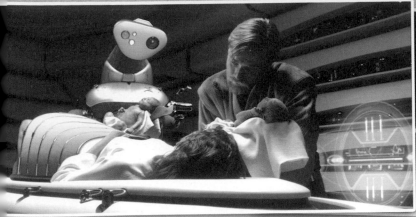

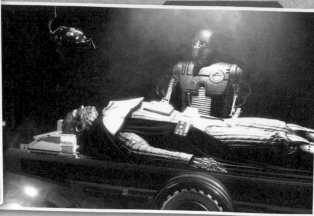

Darth Sidious turned his chair toward Yoda, raised his arms and shot lightning bolts at the Jedi Master, engulfing him. Yoda was picked up by the blast and thrown across the room, where he hit the wall and slid down in a crumpled heap. The Jedi used the Force to throw the Sith Lord back, knocking him clear over his desk. Both ignited their lightsabers and began a fast and furious duel.

The fight raged through vast rooms and into the Senate Chamber, where Sidious dropped his lightsaber and shot another barrage of Sith lightning at Yoda. A lucky blow made Yoda drop his lightsaber and he fell several hundred feet, far away from the Chancellor's evil reach. Yoda had lost the battle but escaped Palpatine with the help of Bail Organa.

Obi-Wan took Padmé to Yoda and Bail Organa and carried her into a medical centre. He was with her as she gave birth to a boy called Luke and then to a girl called Leia. She smiled at her babies, but without Anakin, Padmé no longer had

the strength to go on living. With her last breath she urged Obi-Wan to believe that there was still good in Anakin, but he could not believe it. With one final gasp of pain, Padmé died. Sad and despairing, Bail Organa, Yoda and Obi-Wan sat down to make their plans for the future.

Obi-Wan had no idea that Palpatine had saved Anakin at the last moment. On Coruscant, Anakin's almost lifeless body was encased in a hard black suit, his deformed head covered by a terrible mask. After the medical droids had finished their work, Darth Sidious told his apprentice that he had killed his own wife in his anger. A low groan came from the mask. Suddenly, everything in the room began to implode and Vader's screams of agony echoed throughout the Centre.

Across the galaxy, a small pod raced towards the planet Dagobah, carrying Yoda's tiny form. On the planet of Alderaan, Bail Organa handed baby Leia to his wife. And on Tatooine, Obi-Wan arrived at the home of Owen and Beru Lars, bearing Luke Skywalker in his arms.

JOINING THE DARK SIDE:

A GUIDE TO BEING A SITH

If you wish to join the dark side, you must open your heart to your full range of emotions. Do not try to control your hate, fear and anger because the short-sighted Jedi call them dangerous or negative! They are trying to hide from you the true glory that ultimate power can bring. Power over the galaxy! Power over your subjects! Power over death itself!

Long Live The Sith!

KNOW YOUR ROOTS

The Sith Order began a long time ago, started by a rogue Jedi who was brave enough to experiment with his dark-side powers. When the Jedi Council made it clear that they disapproved and sent him away, this Jedi abandoned the Jedi Order, vowing to one day bring down those who had dismissed him. Other rebellious Jedi joined him, and the Sith Order grew.

After many generations, apprentices were recruited by a very ambitious Sith Master and they waged war on the Jedi and the Republic. The Republic didn't defeat the Sith, the Sith defeated themselves, through in-fighting for power.

The in-fighting weakened the Sith Order for about one thousand years, until a final, bloodthirsty conflict. It seemed that all the Sith had been destroyed. The Jedi declared the Sith Order extinct. However, one Dark Lord called Darth Bane survived in hiding. When he sensed the time was right, he sought out an apprentice. He trained this apprentice, stressing that their enemy was the Jedi Order and not each other.

Eventually, Bane's apprentice became a Sith Master and sought out her own apprentice, thus ensuring that the Sith legacy would survive.

FOLLOW THE BEST EXAMPLE

Darth Sidious stands as one of the most successful Sith of all time. Follow his example! If it hadn't been for the interfering Skywalker clan, the glory of the Sith would never have faded!

SIMPLE STANDARDS

- A Sith exists only to dominate and control.
- Cunning, stealth, and subterfuge should be your watchwords.
- Adapt or die.
- Use your power to control and overpower anyone and anything that stands in the way of ambition and success.

The secret of the Sith who survived was that they contained and concealed their ambitions. They were patient and waited.

The power of the dark side is greater than the power of the light side. When you feel the exhilaration of power, you will want more. This is an individual quest for power, not a co-operative effort!

WEAPONS

Aside from the use of the lightsaber, there are five dark-side disciplines that a true, accomplished Sith must master.

SITH LIGHTNING

One of a Sith's most terrifying powers is the ability to use Sith lightning. It consists of white or blue bolts of pure energy that fly from the user's fingertips towards a target. It causes great pain as it drains the living energy, causes your enemy's muscle groups to seize up, and eventually kills its victim.

As a result of having artificial arms, Darth Vader was never able to up conjure Sith lightning or able to defend himself against it.

FORCE BOLT

This electric bolt can be used to rip through opponents. Its power slows the movements of opponents, making them more vulnerable to attack.

FORCE STORM

This is a Sith lightning attack with increased power. It causes formidable damage and reduces an opponent's ability to evade attacks.

FORCE TEMPEST

The Force tempest erupts into multiple lightning strikes that will course through an opponent's body. It will cause them significant damage and prevent them from escaping.

FORCE MAELSTROM

Shredding an opponent's central nervous system, this lightning attack will render your enemy helpless.

THE PATH TO JEDI STATUS

START
1 > 2 > 3 > 4 > 5 > 6 >

12 > 13 > A RESPECTED JEDI MASTER HAS ACCEPTED YOU AS PADAWAN. CONGRATULATIONS! 14 > 15 > 16 >

23 > 24 > 25 > 26 > 27 > 28 >

34 > 35 > 36 > 37 > 38 > 39

46 > THE FORCE IS STRONG WITH YOU AND YOU HAVE BECOME A JEDI MASTER WITH A PADAWAN OF YOUR OWN 47 > 48 > 49 > 50

54 > 55 > 56 > 57 > 58 > 59

A board game for two or more players.

The aim of the game is to achieve the status of Jedi Master and be invited to join the Council. Journey through the stages of the Jedi Order, avoiding the temptation to give in to the dark side! You will need a marker for each player and a dice.

1. Throw the dice to decide who will go first. The closest to six starts the game.

2. Throw your dice and move your marker along the correct number of spaces.

3. The winner is the first player to fill the remaining space on the Jedi Council. Remember, you must throw exactly the right number to win the game.

7 ›

YOU HAVE BEEN ACCEPTED INTO THE JEDI TEMPLE AS A YOUNGLING. BEGIN TRAINING WITH MASTER YODA AT ONCE!

8 › 9 › 10 › 11 ›

17 › 18 › 19 › 20 › 21 › 22 ›

29 › 30 › 31 › 32 ›

YOU HAVE WORKED HARD AND AT LAST YOU HAVE ACHIEVED THE STATUS OF JEDI KNIGHT.

33 ›

40 › 41 › 42 › 43 › 44 › 45 ›

51 › 52 › 53

60 › 61 › 62 ›

FINISH

GALAXY QUIZ

PART 3

TEST YOUR IDENTIFICATION ABILITIES AND TAKE ON THE NEXT QUIZ LEVEL!

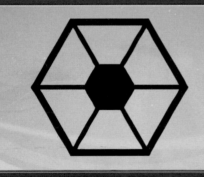

1. Can you identify this symbol?

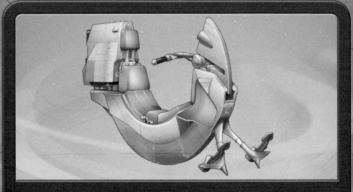

2. Who is the owner of this vehicle?

3. Whose silhouette is this?

4. Name this aquatic vehicle

5. What is the name of this place?

6. Which species wears clothing like this?

7. Who do these eyes belong to?

8. Name this mysterious figure's father.

9. Where is this hut and who lives there?

Yoda

10. Name this woman's granddaughter.

Princess Leia

Check your answers on page 110/111 and add up your score.
(You will always get one point for every correct answer.)

TOTAL SCORE FOR GALAXY QUIZ PART 3

LUKE SKYWALKER

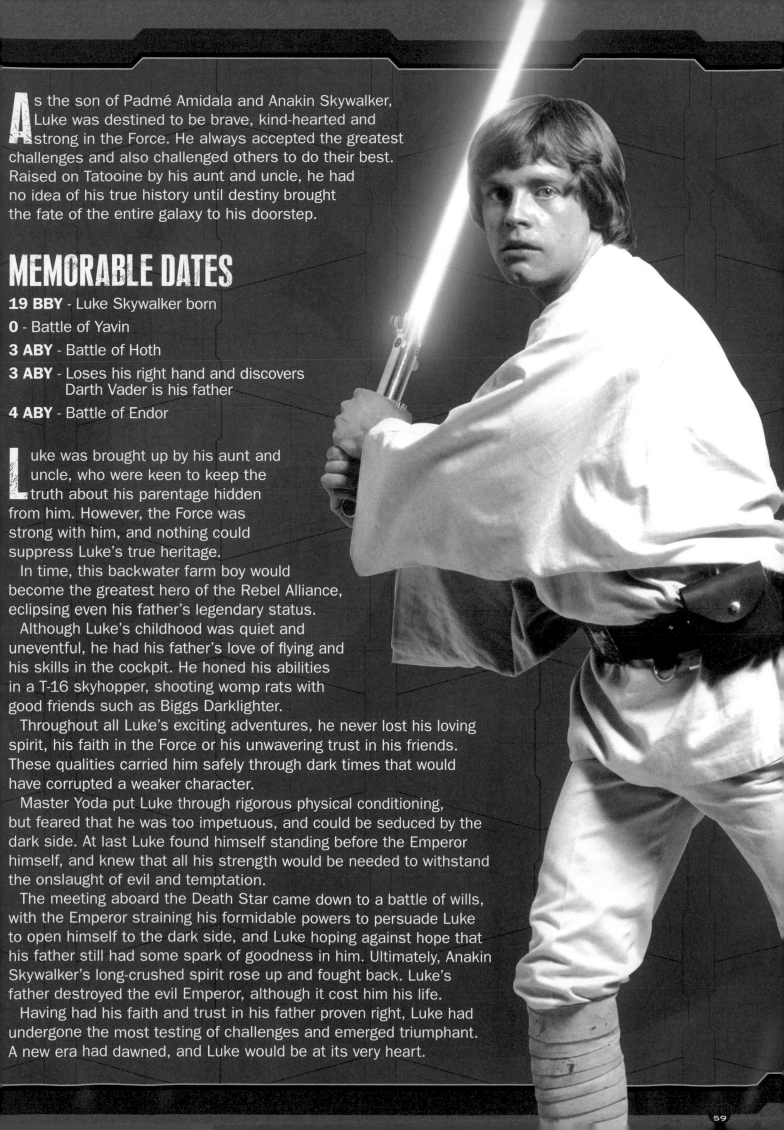

As the son of Padmé Amidala and Anakin Skywalker, Luke was destined to be brave, kind-hearted and strong in the Force. He always accepted the greatest challenges and also challenged others to do their best. Raised on Tatooine by his aunt and uncle, he had no idea of his true history until destiny brought the fate of the entire galaxy to his doorstep.

MEMORABLE DATES

19 BBY - Luke Skywalker born

0 - Battle of Yavin

3 ABY - Battle of Hoth

3 ABY - Loses his right hand and discovers Darth Vader is his father

4 ABY - Battle of Endor

Luke was brought up by his aunt and uncle, who were keen to keep the truth about his parentage hidden from him. However, the Force was strong with him, and nothing could suppress Luke's true heritage.

In time, this backwater farm boy would become the greatest hero of the Rebel Alliance, eclipsing even his father's legendary status.

Although Luke's childhood was quiet and uneventful, he had his father's love of flying and his skills in the cockpit. He honed his abilities in a T-16 skyhopper, shooting womp rats with good friends such as Biggs Darklighter.

Throughout all Luke's exciting adventures, he never lost his loving spirit, his faith in the Force or his unwavering trust in his friends. These qualities carried him safely through dark times that would have corrupted a weaker character.

Master Yoda put Luke through rigorous physical conditioning, but feared that he was too impetuous, and could be seduced by the dark side. At last Luke found himself standing before the Emperor himself, and knew that all his strength would be needed to withstand the onslaught of evil and temptation.

The meeting aboard the Death Star came down to a battle of wills, with the Emperor straining his formidable powers to persuade Luke to open himself to the dark side, and Luke hoping against hope that his father still had some spark of goodness in him. Ultimately, Anakin Skywalker's long-crushed spirit rose up and fought back. Luke's father destroyed the evil Emperor, although it cost him his life.

Having had his faith and trust in his father proven right, Luke had undergone the most testing of challenges and emerged triumphant. A new era had dawned, and Luke would be at its very heart.

PRINCESS LEIA

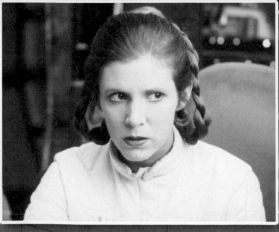

Princess Leia was the daughter of Padmé Amidala and Anakin Skywalker, and Luke's twin sister. Like him, she did not know her true identity, but she grew up as a strong-minded and independent person, enmeshed in the politics of her time and determined to release the galaxy from the Emperor's evil control. She had a deep commitment to peace, freedom and democracy and became the youngest Senator in galactic history.

MEMORABLE DATES

19 BBY - Leia Skywalker born and adopted by Bail Organa of Alderaan

2 BBY - Becomes Senator

0 - Battle of Yavin

3 ABY - Battle of Hoth

4 ABY - Battle of Endor

Princess Leia had the same courage and determination as her twin brother, as well as a fierce commitment to peace, freedom and democracy. She never desired the power that rested on her shoulders, but neither did she reject it. She was always willing to accept the burdens and the risks that it took to accomplish her goals.

Even as a child, Princess Leia was a maverick and a bit of a tomboy. She became one of the most outspoken voices in the Senate, consistently opposing new Imperial policies and condemning the Emperor's many atrocities. Secretly, she was involved in missions for the Rebels, using her consular ship, the *Tantive IV*.

Leia's name remains one of the most revered in galactic history. She had inherited all her mother's sparkling intelligence and wealth of kindness, together with her father's rapier-like wit, passionate nature and unbreakable bravery.

Her courage and intelligence made her a force to be reckoned with, and it is certain that her famous mother would have been proud to call this determined young woman her daughter.

HAN SOLO

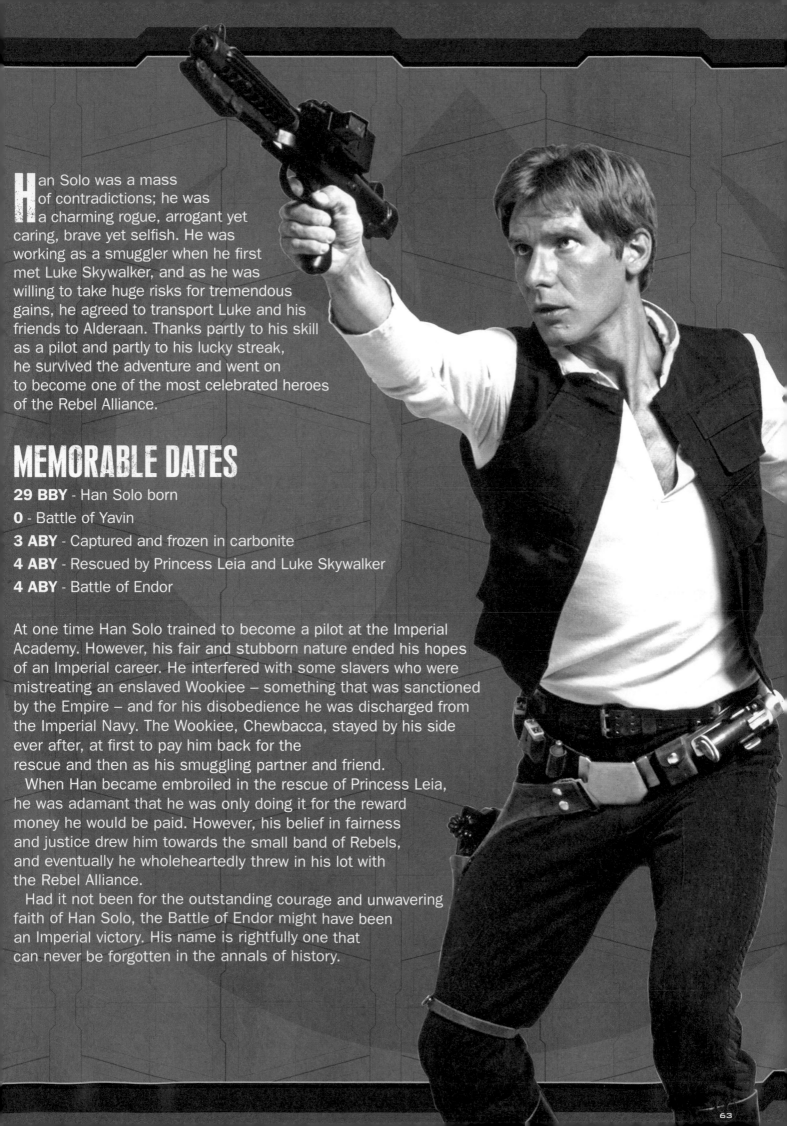

Han Solo was a mass of contradictions; he was a charming rogue, arrogant yet caring, brave yet selfish. He was working as a smuggler when he first met Luke Skywalker, and as he was willing to take huge risks for tremendous gains, he agreed to transport Luke and his friends to Alderaan. Thanks partly to his skill as a pilot and partly to his lucky streak, he survived the adventure and went on to become one of the most celebrated heroes of the Rebel Alliance.

MEMORABLE DATES

29 BBY - Han Solo born

0 - Battle of Yavin

3 ABY - Captured and frozen in carbonite

4 ABY - Rescued by Princess Leia and Luke Skywalker

4 ABY - Battle of Endor

At one time Han Solo trained to become a pilot at the Imperial Academy. However, his fair and stubborn nature ended his hopes of an Imperial career. He interfered with some slavers who were mistreating an enslaved Wookiee – something that was sanctioned by the Empire – and for his disobedience he was discharged from the Imperial Navy. The Wookiee, Chewbacca, stayed by his side ever after, at first to pay him back for the rescue and then as his smuggling partner and friend.

When Han became embroiled in the rescue of Princess Leia, he was adamant that he was only doing it for the reward money he would be paid. However, his belief in fairness and justice drew him towards the small band of Rebels, and eventually he wholeheartedly threw in his lot with the Rebel Alliance.

Had it not been for the outstanding courage and unwavering faith of Han Solo, the Battle of Endor might have been an Imperial victory. His name is rightfully one that can never be forgotten in the annals of history.

THE SKYWALKER CLAN

Civil war wracked the galaxy, and every planet and being who helped the Rebels lived under the threat of Imperial retaliation. Desperate to find some chink in their enemy's formidable armour, Rebel spies managed to steal secret plans to the Empire's ultimate weapon, the Death Star. This gigantic space station had enough power to explode entire planets, and if the Rebels could destroy it, they would have struck a truly decisive blow against the Empire.

Chased by the Emperor's second in command, Darth Vader, Senator Princess Leia was trying to reach her home planet with the stolen plans. However, the Imperial ship was too fast for them, and soon caught up. Darth Vader seized Princess Leia, but not before she was able to give the Death Star plans and a message to R2-D2, who escaped with C-3PO. Darth Vader prepared to torture the Princess for information on board the Death Star, little guessing that she was his own flesh and blood.

R2-D2 and C-3PO landed on the nearby planet of Tatooine, and after a series of traumatic adventures they were purchased by Owen and Beru Lars. Owen told his nephew, Luke Skywalker, to clean the new droids up and set them to work.

While Luke was cleaning R2-D2, he dislodged part of a hidden message from the Princess. She had recorded it moments before she was captured, begging Obi-Wan Kenobi for help. Luke tried to discover more, but to his frustration, R2-D2 claimed ignorance of the message.

A princess in distress! This was the kind of adventure that Luke had longed for all his life. Dreaming of the girl's lovely face, he left the droids and went to have his dinner. He had never been told the truth about his father, so when he mentioned the message to his aunt and uncle, they were worried.

While Luke was at dinner, R2-D2 went off in search of Obi-Wan Kenobi, who lived on the other side of the Dune Sea. The next morning, Luke and C-3PO searched for the little astromech droid. They found him and then encountered Obi-Wan Kenobi, who told Luke that his father was a Jedi Knight and a great star pilot. Luke learned that his father, Anakin Skywalker, was killed by the evil Darth Vader, who was once Obi-Wan's Padawan pupil. Obi-Wan gave Luke his father's lightsaber and told him about the Force.

R2-D2 played the message from the Princess. Luke watched and listened in wonder as she begged Obi-Wan to take the plans of the Death Star to her father on Alderaan. Obi-Wan asked Luke to join him and go to Alderaan, but Luke refused. As much as he longed for adventure, he knew that he had a duty to his uncle.

However, when they returned to the Lars farm, everything changed. They found it had been torched by Vader's stormtroopers, who were searching for the droids. Luke's aunt and uncle were dead, and Luke had no one left. Despite his grief and confusion, he decided at once to join Obi-Wan on his mission to Alderaan. He wanted to learn the ways of the Force and become a Jedi Knight, like his father.

The travellers went to Mos Eisley spaceport, where Obi-Wan hired a pilot to take them to Alderaan in his ship. Their pilot was a charming rogue called Han Solo, and he and his Wookiee first mate, Chewbacca, had a fast starship called the *Millennium Falcon*. Han owed money to the gangster Jabba the Hutt, and was keen to get away before Jabba had him found by a bounty hunter.

In the meantime, Darth Vader's stormtroopers had located the droids and their companions and they fired on the *Millennium Falcon* as it left Tatooine. Fortunately the ship escaped into hyperspace and travelled at light speed towards Alderaan.

The Death Star had reached Alderaan, Princess Leia's home planet. She was told that if she did not reveal the location of the Rebel base, Alderaan would be destroyed. She told them that the base was on Dantooine, but they blew up Alderaan anyway, killing all her people and her family. Leia despaired as tiny pieces of her homeworld exploded into space. She had lied about the location of the Rebel base, so she was placed in the detention cells to await execution.

As Alderaan exploded, Obi-Wan felt a terrible disturbance in the Force. The *Falcon* came out of light speed and the crew saw only the Death Star where Alderaan should have been. Before they could escape, the Death Star drew them in with a tractor beam. They were now in the heart of the enemy's territory.

Han, Luke and Chewbacca overpowered the guards and hid in the battle station, but Darth Vader sensed Obi-Wan's presence. Once he had loved his old Master like a brother, but now he wanted nothing more than to destroy Obi-Wan, as he believed Obi-Wan had destroyed him.

While Obi-Wan left to deactivate the tractor beam that was holding them, R2-D2 discovered that the Princess was on board and was being held prisoner. Much against Han's better judgement, Luke insisted that they rescue her. After a series of narrow escapes, they managed to rescue her from the detention cell. Within a very short time, Leia and Han were infuriating one another and Luke was feeling a bewilderingly powerful connection to this beautiful girl.

Obi-Wan found the power terminal and shut it down, deactivating the tractor beam that was holding the *Millennium Falcon*. Luke, Leia, Han and Chewbacca battled past storm troopers and at last reached the ship... but Obi-Wan did not join them. He had come face to face with Darth Vader.

The two men ignited their lightsabers. After long years, they battled once again. However, this time Obi-Wan was an old man, and Darth Vader was half-machine. Besides, the others needed a distraction if they were going to escape. Obi-Wan held up his lightsaber and closed his eyes, accepting his destiny at the hands of his old Padawan. Darth Vader struck him down and his body vanished.

Darth Vader allowed the *Millennium Falcon* to escape, but commanded the Death Star to follow it. The *Falcon* led them to Yavin 4, the headquarters of the Rebellion. Now there was no time to lose. With the plans that Princess Leia had brought them, the Rebels identified a weakness in the Death Star. However, the target area was only two metres wide. A precise hit on the thermal exhaust port would destroy the entire battle station, but it would take a gifted pilot to make the hit.

Luke decided to pilot an X-wing fighter, and sped into space with the other Rebel pilots to engage the enemy. Darth Vader was piloting his own fighter, and had lost none of his flair and skill. Against him, the Rebel fighters didn't stand a chance . . . until he was pitted against Luke Skywalker.

With only a minute left before the Death Star would be in range to destroy Yavin 4, Luke heard the voice of Obi-Wan Kenobi telling him to use the Force to aim his weapon at the tiny target. Luke switched off his guidance computer and let the Force guide him instead. The Rebel leaders could not understand what he was doing, but Darth Vader sensed at once that the Force was incredibly strong with this boy.

Despite Luke's skilled flying, Darth Vader was close on his tail and it looked as though he could not escape. Then, without warning, the *Millennium Falcon* appeared above Vader and blasted his fighter, sending him whirling into space. In the Rebels' hour of need, Han was a hero!

Luke launched his proton torpedoes into the target using the Force. The Death Star exploded into millions of tiny burning pieces. Together, Luke, Leia, Chewbacca and Han had created a new hope – a hope that the Empire could one day be destroyed.

A Jedi maintains an open channel of communication with the Living Force, and is always approachable and welcoming. On the other hand, if you have turned to the dark side your Sith nature will want to keep friends and family away. Which side will you choose?

A JEDI'S FRIENDS ARE ALWAYS WELCOME - PLEASE KNOCK AND ENTER.

SIDE

KEEP OUT

SITH IN TRAINING.

1. Trim a piece of thick white card to the right shape

2. Trace the design onto the white card

3. Trace the other side of the hanger on to the other side of the card

4. Use colouring pens to bring your images to life

5. Place the hanger over your bedroom door knob to show which side you have chosen

SITH SEEKER

USE YOUR JEDI SKILLS AND YOUR STRENGTH IN THE FORCE TO LOCATE THESE FAMOUS SITH NAMES AND IMPORTANT WORDS.

- [ ] BANE
- [ ] CONTROL
- [ ] DARK
- [ ] DARTH
- [ ] EVIL
- [ ] MAUL
- [ ] POWER
- [ ] SIDIOUS
- [ ] TYRANUS
- [ ] VADER

A	F	B	E	C	G	H	D	K	C	E	F	N	I	C
L	J	L	U	A	M	P	G	H	A	J	E	F	L	E
C	I	D	H	D	M	E	C	N	D	D	B	G	V	K
K	A	G	P	A	C	D	A	R	T	H	J	I	I	E
G	H	P	B	L	G	B	J	C	G	L	L	G	B	H
E	E	G	A	I	D	I	L	A	H	C	C	M	D	L
A	M	F	E	C	F	B	I	N	B	F	M	H	O	H
J	S	K	T	Y	R	A	N	U	S	B	E	R	G	C
C	U	F	D	I	P	N	K	N	E	R	T	R	K	A
G	O	B	P	G	E	E	C	E	L	N	E	V	O	F
H	I	O	E	O	G	N	A	O	O	N	B	A	D	G
F	D	C	N	F	W	P	G	C	I	C	K	D	O	B
I	I	E	D	I	E	E	J	D	B	O	A	E	F	I
L	S	H	O	A	K	L	R	C	M	R	G	R	L	A
A	F	O	F	H	C	M	A	F	K	J	B	H	I	D

CHALLENGE:
QUOTE COMPLETION

CAN YOU REMEMBER WHO SAID THESE MEMORABLE WORDS?

1 :: "Either I'm going to kill her or I'm beginning to like her."

2 :: "You have become the very thing you swore to destroy."

3 :: "The dark side of the Force is a pathway to many abilities some consider to be unnatural."

4 :: "When 900 years old you reach, look as good you will not. Hmm?"

Yoda

5 :: "At last we will reveal ourselves to the Jedi. At last we will have revenge."

6 :: "Your focus determines your reality."

7 :: "Anakin, you're breaking my heart!"

8 :: "Fear is the path to the dark side. Fear leads to anger; anger leads to hate; hate leads to suffering. I sense much fear in you."

Yoda

9 :: "I'll never turn to the dark side... I am a Jedi, like my father before me."

10 :: And for a final bonus point, of whom was Han Solo talking when he said: "He's a card player, gambler, scoundrel. You'd like him."?

GALAXY QUIZ

PART 4

PUSH YOUR MEMORY AND KNOWLEDGE TO THE
LIMIT AS YOU TAKE ON THE NEXT QUIZ LEVEL!

1. Identify each badge and match it with the person who wears it.

A

B

C

D

1

2

3

4

2. What is a very familiar phrase spoken between Jedi, usually when they are parting company?

May the force be with you

3. Name three things a Padawan will have about his or her person.

4. Name three things you need in order to travel at lightspeed.

74

5. Examine these pictures. Can you name each vessel and identify its owner?

VESSEL   OWNER

VESSEL   OWNER

VESSEL   OWNER

VESSEL   OWNER

6. Identify the five Force powers that a Sith is prepared to use.

7. How many Jedi have voluntarily left the Order?

8. If your chief is Boss Nass, what species are you?

9. What is Poggle the Lesser's home planet?

10. Name three of the twelve members of the Jedi Council at the time of the Battle of Geonosis.

Check your answers on page 110/111 and add up your score.
(You will always get one point for every correct answer.)

TOTAL SCORE FOR GALAXY QUIZ PART 4

R2-D2

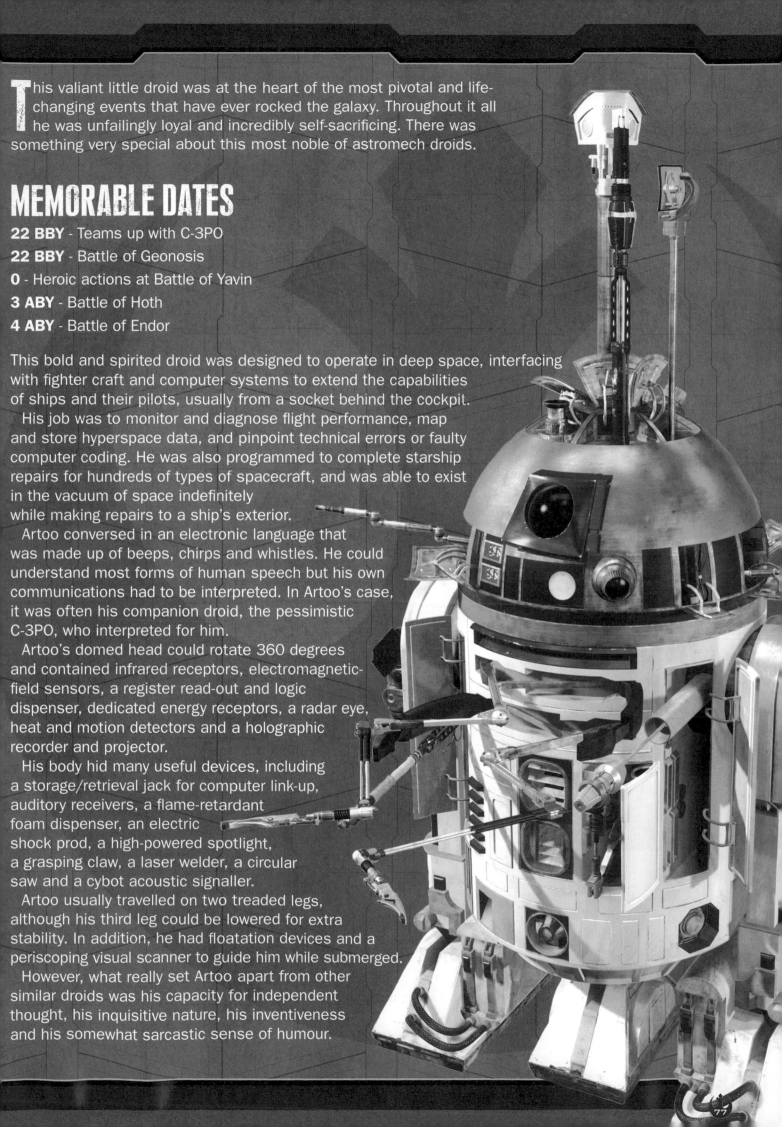

This valiant little droid was at the heart of the most pivotal and life-changing events that have ever rocked the galaxy. Throughout it all he was unfailingly loyal and incredibly self-sacrificing. There was something very special about this most noble of astromech droids.

MEMORABLE DATES

22 BBY - Teams up with C-3PO
22 BBY - Battle of Geonosis
0 - Heroic actions at Battle of Yavin
3 ABY - Battle of Hoth
4 ABY - Battle of Endor

This bold and spirited droid was designed to operate in deep space, interfacing with fighter craft and computer systems to extend the capabilities of ships and their pilots, usually from a socket behind the cockpit.

His job was to monitor and diagnose flight performance, map and store hyperspace data, and pinpoint technical errors or faulty computer coding. He was also programmed to complete starship repairs for hundreds of types of spacecraft, and was able to exist in the vacuum of space indefinitely while making repairs to a ship's exterior.

Artoo conversed in an electronic language that was made up of beeps, chirps and whistles. He could understand most forms of human speech but his own communications had to be interpreted. In Artoo's case, it was often his companion droid, the pessimistic C-3PO, who interpreted for him.

Artoo's domed head could rotate 360 degrees and contained infrared receptors, electromagnetic-field sensors, a register read-out and logic dispenser, dedicated energy receptors, a radar eye, heat and motion detectors and a holographic recorder and projector.

His body hid many useful devices, including a storage/retrieval jack for computer link-up, auditory receivers, a flame-retardant foam dispenser, an electric shock prod, a high-powered spotlight, a grasping claw, a laser welder, a circular saw and a cybot acoustic signaller.

Artoo usually travelled on two treaded legs, although his third leg could be lowered for extra stability. In addition, he had floatation devices and a periscoping visual scanner to guide him while submerged.

However, what really set Artoo apart from other similar droids was his capacity for independent thought, his inquisitive nature, his inventiveness and his somewhat sarcastic sense of humour.

YODA

A legend in his own time, Master Yoda was small in height but great in the Force. He lived for more than 900 years, and at least 800 of those years were spent training Jedi Knights in the ways of the Force. His wisdom, insight and whimsical teaching style were unique and joyful to all those who knew him.

MEMORABLE DATES

896 BBY - Yoda born

22 BBY - Battle of Geonosis

19 BBY - Loses battle with Palpatine and goes into hiding

3 ABY - Trains Luke Skywalker

4 ABY - Becomes one with the Force

Yoda's path to Jedi wisdom was simple and yet profound. He gently guided his students to unlearn what they had been taught and tune in to the world around them to learn its truths.

As one of the most experienced members of the Jedi Council, Yoda's advice and opinions carried great weight among his peers. In his earlier life he had travelled across the galaxy, visiting hundreds of worlds in his quest to understand the Force.

By the time Anakin Skywalker burst upon the Jedi Council, Yoda was more than 800-years-old. He had grown thoughtful and deliberate, preferring to take his time and weigh facts before impulsively rushing to make a decision. He could sense dangerous emotions in Anakin Skywalker – emotions that Yoda knew could lead the boy to the dark side of the Force.

Yoda's skill with a lightsaber was second to none on the Council, but he had underestimated the vicious Sith skills of Palpatine. When he lost his lightsaber duel with Palpatine, Yoda went into hiding on Dagobah and used the planet's natural defences to discourage visitors. He used his connection with the Force to keep watch on Luke Skywalker and Leia Organa.

C-ЭPO

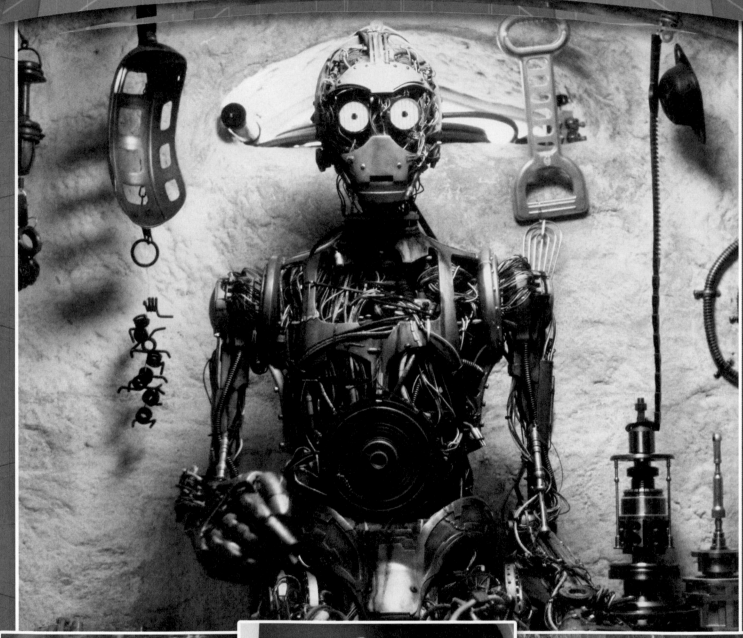

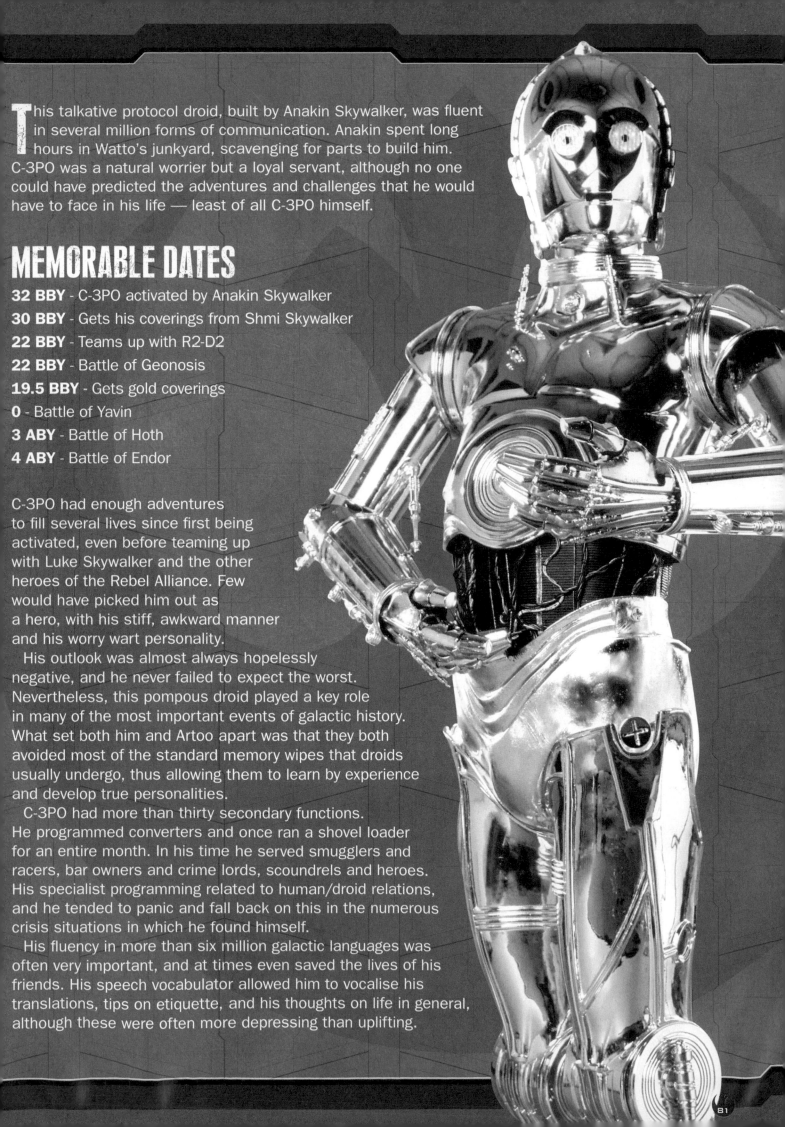

This talkative protocol droid, built by Anakin Skywalker, was fluent in several million forms of communication. Anakin spent long hours in Watto's junkyard, scavenging for parts to build him. C-3PO was a natural worrier but a loyal servant, although no one could have predicted the adventures and challenges that he would have to face in his life — least of all C-3PO himself.

MEMORABLE DATES

32 BBY - C-3PO activated by Anakin Skywalker

30 BBY - Gets his coverings from Shmi Skywalker

22 BBY - Teams up with R2-D2

22 BBY - Battle of Geonosis

19.5 BBY - Gets gold coverings

0 - Battle of Yavin

3 ABY - Battle of Hoth

4 ABY - Battle of Endor

C-3PO had enough adventures to fill several lives since first being activated, even before teaming up with Luke Skywalker and the other heroes of the Rebel Alliance. Few would have picked him out as a hero, with his stiff, awkward manner and his worry wart personality.

His outlook was almost always hopelessly negative, and he never failed to expect the worst. Nevertheless, this pompous droid played a key role in many of the most important events of galactic history. What set both him and Artoo apart was that they both avoided most of the standard memory wipes that droids usually undergo, thus allowing them to learn by experience and develop true personalities.

C-3PO had more than thirty secondary functions. He programmed converters and once ran a shovel loader for an entire month. In his time he served smugglers and racers, bar owners and crime lords, scoundrels and heroes. His specialist programming related to human/droid relations, and he tended to panic and fall back on this in the numerous crisis situations in which he found himself.

His fluency in more than six million galactic languages was often very important, and at times even saved the lives of his friends. His speech vocabulator allowed him to vocalise his translations, tips on etiquette, and his thoughts on life in general, although these were often more depressing than uplifting.

IMPERIAL REVENGE

After the destruction of the Death Star, the Empire was bent on revenge. Its clone troops chased the Rebel forces across the galaxy, determined to wipe the rebellion out once and for all. Desperate to find a safe hiding place where they could regroup and make new plans, Luke Skywalker helped build a new base for himself and the Rebel freedom fighters on Hoth, an ice planet far from any other civilisation. Meanwhile, Darth Vader had become obsessed with finding Luke. He sent thousands of remote probes into space, all programmed to seek out this boy who was so strong in the Force.

Han and Luke had just finished a routine area check of the freezing ice world. Although Han returned to the base, Luke saw one of Vader's probes land on the planet surface. When he went to check, a terrible snow beast attacked him and dragged him away.

At the base, Han was about to leave so that he could pay off Jabba the Hutt. Leia was furious with Han for leaving and they argued until they heard the news that Luke had not returned. This was so serious that all arguments were forgotten. If Luke did not return before nightfall, he would die out in the snowy wastes of Hoth.

Their happiness was short-lived. On board his starship, Darth Vader had received a transmission from his probe and set a course for Hoth. Luckily for the Rebels, sensors at the base intercepted the transmission. They realised the Empire knew where they were and had to evacuate the base.

The Rebel forces agreed on a rendezvous point and prepared to leave, but Darth Vader sent his troops down to the planet for a surface attack as the Rebel forces tried desperately to escape. There was a tremendous battle between the Rebels and the Imperial stormtroopers as the Rebel forces were evacuated. Luke helped to fight the Imperial ground troops and risked his life to destroy their walkers. But he had not forgotten his vision. As soon as the Rebels had evacuated, he escaped in his X-wing fighter with R2-D2 and set a course for the Dagobah system.

Han went to search for his friend, who had been dragged to the beast's cave. Luke managed to use his lightsaber to free himself and escape, but he collapsed in the freezing snow. Then he saw Obi-Wan Kenobi standing in front of him.

The vision of Obi-Wan told him to go to the Dagobah system, where he would learn from Yoda, a Jedi Master. As Obi-Wan faded away, Luke passed out. But Han found him just in time and saved his life, returning to the base the following morning to the astonishment and delight of everyone.

Darth Vader hired bounty hunters to capture the *Millennium Falcon* and then reported to the Emperor. He was shocked to learn that Luke was his own son, but even this knowledge could not break through the barriers he had put up against his own past. The Emperor told him that the son of Skywalker must not become a Jedi, because the Force was so strong with him that he could destroy them. But if they could turn him to the dark side, he would be a powerful ally.

Even though the *Millennium Falcon*'s hyperdrive was damaged Han and Chewbacca escaped just in time with Princess Leia and C-3PO. Darth Vader was furious. He sent starships after them, but Han managed to lose them in an asteroid field. Thinking that he had outwitted his enemies, Han set a course for a nearby mining colony,

which was run by his friend, Lando Calrissian. There they would find the parts they needed to repair the *Millennium Falcon*'s hyperdrive. However, Han and Chewbacca did not know that the bounty hunter Boba Fett was following them.

Luke crash-landed in a swamp on Dagobah and set up camp in a clearing, wondering if he was crazy to have travelled so far on the basis of a vision. Then he met a small, comical person with green skin and large ears. Luke explained that he was looking for a great warrior, and the little being promised to take him to Yoda.

Eventually, after Luke had displayed his impatience and temper, the green creature revealed that he was Yoda. Luke was shocked and humbled, and he promised to work as hard as he could, if Yoda would agree to train him. After much persuasion, Yoda agreed.

Luke found his training very tough. He learned that a Jedi's strength flows from the Force. He learned that anger, fear and aggression lead to the dark side of the Force. He knew that he had to learn to stay calm and use the Force for knowledge and defence – never for attack. But even Yoda was unsure whether or not the boy could overcome his fear and doubts.

The *Millennium Falcon* landed at the mining colony, which was a beautiful city in the clouds. Han's friend Lando greeted them, but Leia was suspicious of him. Han would not believe that his friend could be false, but he did not know that Lando was trying to save all his people from torture and oppression. Boba Fett had led Vader to the city and Lando had been given a choice – save his people or save his friends. After a few days Lando handed his friends over to Darth Vader.

Meanwhile, Luke was improving – he was learning to feel the Force and managing to stay calm. But in the midst of his training he had a vision of Han and Leia in danger in a city in the clouds. He lost his concentration and decided that he had to go and help them. Yoda warned him against leaving before completing his training – it was too dangerous. Obi-Wan's spirit appeared and also tried to persuade him. They said that only a fully trained Jedi Knight could conquer Darth Vader and the Emperor. But it was no use. Luke promised to return and complete his training, but he could not stand by and let his friends suffer. He left with R2-D2 to help his friends.

Darth Vader knew that Luke would come to rescue his friends. He planned to put Luke in a carbon-freezing facility and take him to the Emperor, but first he tested it on Han, who was frozen solid in carbonite. Darth Vader gave Han to Boba Fett, who planned to take him to Jabba the Hutt and collect the reward.

When Luke and R2-D2 arrived at the mining colony, he saw Lando and a group of stormtroopers leading Leia, C-3PO and Chewbacca away. Luke followed them into a hangar, but it was a trap. Luke turned and saw the black figure of Darth Vader. They ignited their lightsabers and began to duel.

Lando, guilt-stricken at what he had done, freed Leia, C-3PO and Chewbacca. They found R2-D2 and fought their way past stormtroopers to the *Millennium Falcon*. Just in the nick of time, they flew away to safety.

While his friends were escaping, Luke was defending himself well against the Dark Lord of the Sith. However, Darth Vader was a more skilful warrior. Finally Luke fell onto a platform above a bottomless drop. Darth Vader swiped cruelly at him with his red lightsaber and cut off his right hand, which plummeted over the edge of the platform and disappeared into the darkness. Luke looked up, believing that these were his last moments. Instead, however, Darth Vader revealed something that shook Luke's world into pieces.

"I am your father," he said.

Luke was horrified. His thoughts whirled as Vader told him that it was his destiny to turn to the dark side and help destroy the Emperor so that they could rule the galaxy together as father and son. But despite his spinning thoughts and his confusion, Luke knew that he would rather die than turn to the dark side. He rolled over the edge of the platform and dropped into the abyss.

Far below, Luke broke his fall by clinging to a metal structure below the city. Something made him use the Force to call to Leia, sure that she would hear him. On the *Millennium Falcon*, Leia heard him and ordered Lando and Chewbacca to turn the ship around. Darth Vader sensed that Luke was still alive and tried to prevent the rescue, but they entered hyperspace and escaped with Luke at light speed. A new chapter of history had been finished.

JOINING THE GOOD SIDE:

A GUIDE TO BEING A JEDI

The Jedi Order is a brave and noble group whose members are linked by their belief and trust in the Force. They strive to uphold their ideals of peace, love and fairness throughout the galaxy. To become a Jedi is to devote your life to the well-being and care of others. It is not a step to be taken lightly, and it is not a lifestyle that weak or fearful people can sustain. Beware! If you enter the Temple and commit yourself to training as a Jedi, your deepest thoughts and feelings will be known by your Masters. The Jedi Order is no place for secrets.

THE FORCE

This is the mystical energy field that binds all living things. A Jedi's strength flows from the Force, but a true Jedi uses it only for knowledge and defence, never for attack. Through the Force, a Jedi Knight can see far-off places and accomplish seemingly impossible feats.

Jedi receive their amazing powers by tapping into the Force. Microscopic symbionts, called midi-chlorians, form the connection between all living beings and the Force. There are two sides to the Force. The light side gives great knowledge, peace and inner calm. However, the dark side is filled with fear, anger and aggression. Both sides of the Force are a necessary part of the natural order, and both are needed for true balance to exist within the galaxy.

FORBIDDEN

- Personal ornamentation such as jewellery
- Possession
- Marriage

JEDI PHILOSOPHY

- Jedi are the guardians of peace in the galaxy.
- Jedi use their powers to learn and to protect, never to attack others.
- Jedi respect all life, in any form.
- Jedi serve others rather than ruling over them, for the good of the galaxy.
- Jedi seek to improve themselves through knowledge and training.
- A Jedi does not act for personal power or wealth but seeks knowledge and enlightenment.
- A Jedi never acts from hatred, anger, fear or aggression but acts when calm and at peace with the Force.

TRAINING

- Jedi train in clans from the age of four until the age of eight.
- At eight, they embark upon individual advanced training with a Jedi Master.
- At the age of ten, a Jedi is assigned to another Master as a Padawan. Between the ages of nineteen and twenty-two, a Padawan goes through the Jedi trials. When the Master believes the Padawan to be ready, the Padawan will undertake a final trial and gain the status of Jedi Knight.
- Becoming a Master can happen at any age, as it is dependent upon a Jedi's personal accomplishments and varying achievements.

FORCE SKILLS

There are three major Force skills – control, sense, and alter. Only Force-sensitive beings can master Jedi skills and techniques, but the training to reach full Jedi status usually requires a great deal of time and patience.

CONTROL

The ability of a Jedi to master his or her own inner Force, which includes the functions of his or her own body.

SENSE

Helps Jedi become aware of the Force in things beyond themselves, and to feel the bonds that connect all things.

ALTER

Allows a Jedi to change the nature of the Force to create illusions, move objects or modify the perceptions of others.

THE JEDI CODE

There is no emotion;
there is peace.

There is no ignorance;
there is knowledge.

There is no passion;
there is serenity.

THE FOURTH PRECEPT

There is no death;
there is only the Force.

MOMENTS IN TIME

LOOK AT THESE PICTURES. DO YOU KNOW WHAT WAS HAPPENING IN EACH EXCITING SCENE? FILL IN A DETAILED DESCRIPTION UNDERNEATH EACH IMAGE.

Young Aniken getting ready for the podrace. If he wins then the broken parts for the Jedi's ship can be fixed or replaced.

Luke Skywalker, Chewbacca and Han Solo rescue Princess Leia. They go through a hatch to escape and end up in a garbage room which crushes the garbage.

Luke Skywalker fighting with Darth Vader and finding out he is his father.

GALAXY QUIZ

PART 5

THIS CHALLENGE WILL TEST YOUR VALUES AND JUDGEMENT.

2. You are losing a lightsaber duel and you know that death is upon you. How do you feel?

A. Terrified

B. Calm and ready for the next great adventure

C. Furious

1. You sense a terrible disturbance in the Force. What do you do?

A. Destroy the source of the disturbance

B. Inform the Jedi Council and await instructions

C. Nothing – someone else will deal with it

B

3. What is most important to you?

A. Your connection with the living Force

B. Your lightsaber – it is the most elegant one possessed by any Jedi

C. Your friends and family

4. Your Jedi Master has been reported missing, believed dead. The Jedi Council orders you to go to a different part of the galaxy to lead a battle. What do you do?

A. Disobey the Council's orders and go to search for your Master

B. Trust the Council and follow their orders

C. Tell a Council member that you wish to search for your Master and ask for their help in persuading the Council

C

5. What is your attitude to the dark side?

A. It is a necessary danger, and you will guard against it with all the strength you have

B. It terrifies you

C. You find it interesting and wish you understood more about it

A

6. Someone is spreading lies about you through the galaxy, and you are losing friends. What do you do?

A. Stay calm and use the Force to identify the liar so you can expose the truth

B. Go into hiding

C. Do everything you can to find the liar so that you can challenge him or her to a lightsaber duel

A

Check your answers on page 110/111 and add up your score.
(You will always get one point for every correct answer.)

TOTAL SCORE FOR GALAXY QUIZ PART 5   18

CHALLENGE: LINKS

NAME EACH OF THESE CHARACTERS AND THEN WORK OUT WHAT SINGLE ROMANTIC EVENT LINKS THEM ALL TOGETHER.

1

2

3

4

5

6

7

THE SINGLE EVENT THAT LINKS THEM ALL TOGETHER IS:

Hint: Whose marriage connects all these characters?

:: 1 ::

:: 2 ::

:: 3 ::

:: 4 ::

:: 5 ::

:: 6 ::

:: 7 ::

NEWS CHANNEL

Can you guess what the missing words are from these items of headline news?

SENATOR PADMÉ AMIDALA [____] OF A BROKEN [____] .

[____] TWINS IDENTIFIED AFTER [____] YEARS IN [____] .

MASTER YODA [____] AT THE AGE OF [____] .

SHOCKING NEWS FOR LUKE SKYWALKER: [____] IS HIS [____] !

THE CLUMSIEST [____] ALIVE RETURNS TO

OTOH [____] – [____] [____] IS FURIOUS.

QUEEN [____] AND [____] NASS

JOIN [____] AGAINST COMMON [____] .

ENDOR CELEBRATES AS [____] SAVE THE [____] .

ORDER [____] IS CARRIED OUT

AND [____] ARE NO MORE.

BRAVE ASTROMECH [____] SAVES THE PLANS

OF THE [____] : [____] IS A REBEL HERO!

THE [____] PLANS TO PERSONALLY OVERSEE THE

CONSTRUCTION OF THE [____] DEATH STAR.

96

GRID
DRAWING

Use this grid guide to create your own picture of the mysterious Boba Fett.

THE JEDI RETURN

The Galactic Empire had rapidly begun building a new Death Star. When completed, this weapon would spell doom for the Rebels struggling to free the galaxy.

On Tatooine, Luke, Leia and Lando carried out a daring plan to rescue Han from Jabba the Hutt. Even the droids joined the team and helped to rescue Han, who had been hanging on Jabba's wall in carbonite. Furious, Jabba tried to throw the friends into the pit of Carkoon, but he was defeated and killed, and Boba Fett was thrown into the pit instead.

Reunited at last, Leia and Han flew to meet the Rebel Alliance with Lando, Chewbacca and C-3PO. But Luke and R2-D2 set a course for the Dagobah system. Luke had a promise to Yoda and Obi-Wan to keep.

On the half-completed Death Star, Lord Vader's shuttle arrived in the landing bay. He bore frightening news for the commander: The Emperor himself was coming to oversee the creation of the battle station. The black-cloaked Emperor arrived, greeted Darth Vader and told him to bring Luke to him. He had grown stronger, and only together could they turn him to the dark side of the Force.

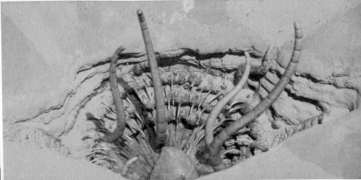

When Luke returned to Dagobah, he found Yoda dying. Yoda told Luke that he needed no more training, but that he must confront Darth Vader before he could truly be considered a Jedi. He reminded Luke that a Jedi's strength flows from the Force. Then his body vanished, just as Obi-Wan's had after his battle with Darth Vader. Both legendary Jedi had joined the Force.

As Luke grieved for his Master, Obi-Wan appeared next to him. He was sorry that Luke had found out the truth about the identity of his father, because he knew that it was a terrible burden. He explained that when Anakin had been seduced by the dark side of the Force, he had ceased to be Anakin Skywalker and became Darth Vader.

Luke was overcome with pity for his father. Like his long-dead mother, he found it impossible to believe that someone who had once been so good could have become completely evil. He refused to agree to kill him.

Obi-Wan was worried, and believed that this meant the Emperor could win. He also told Luke that he had a twin sister, and Luke's insight revealed to him that his sister was Leia. He returned to rendezvous with the Rebels, feeling older, sadder and wiser.

The Rebels were making their final plans to attack the Empire. They had learned that in order to destroy the Death Star, they had to deactivate its energy shield. The energy shield was powered from the forest moon of Endor.

Han was commissioned to lead the strike team to Endor with Luke, Leia and Chewbacca. Lando was going to lead the attack on the Death Star. Han lent Lando the *Millennium Falcon*, then set off for Endor with his strike team.

As soon as Han's strike team landed on Endor, Darth Vader sensed that Luke was there. He told the Emperor, who ordered him to go down to Endor and wait for Luke. Palpatine had foreseen that Luke would seek his father out. His evil plans were advancing just as he had hoped.

On the forest-covered moon, the strike team befriended a tribe of Ewoks. Safe for the evening in the Ewoks' tree top village, Luke told Leia that she was his twin sister and that Darth Vader was their father. Leia was stunned, her emotions in turmoil. As she mused over these facts, Luke added that Darth Vader could sense his presence, and so he had to leave the strike team because he was putting them in danger.

Knowing that destiny was leading him now, Luke surrendered to the Imperial troops and was taken to Darth Vader. He told the Sith Lord that deep down he was still Anakin Skywalker. Vader hesitated, feeling emotions he had not acknowledged for years. Luke could sense the conflict within his father and urged him to let go of his hate, but Vader shook himself free of Luke's persuasion and said that he had to obey his master.

Darth Vader took Luke to the Emperor on board the Death Star. The Emperor revealed that he knew about the Alliance attack – Luke's friends were walking into a trap and he could do nothing to save them.

The *Millennium Falcon* was in position with the Alliance fleet. Everything was ready for the attack. They entered lightspeed and set their course for Endor. But on Endor, Han and the strike team

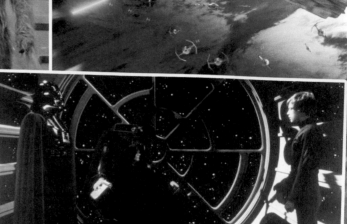

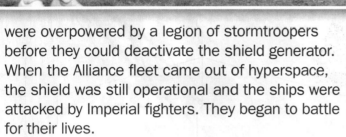

were overpowered by a legion of stormtroopers before they could deactivate the shield generator. When the Alliance fleet came out of hyperspace, the shield was still operational and the ships were attacked by Imperial fighters. They began to battle for their lives.

From the Death Star, Luke watched the fight in despair. The Emperor tried to encourage Luke to give in to his anger, but Luke refused, keeping his rage under control.

On Endor, Han and his team were led away by Imperial troops. But suddenly the troops were attacked by the brave little Ewoks! Hundreds of the bold creatures rose out of their hiding places in the undergrowth with bows and arrows. A massive battle began on the planet's surface as Leia and Han raced back to the shield generator.

The Alliance ships were being destroyed by the overwhelming firepower of the terrible Death Star. The Alliance commander, Admiral Ackbar, wanted to retreat, but Lando trusted Han to deactivate the shield. He insisted they hold their position.

The Emperor told Luke that the rebellion was lost and that his friends would die. He did everything he could to antagonise the young man, and was pleased when he felt Luke's anger bubbling. Anger leads to the dark side, and if he could only persuade Luke to let his anger show, he knew that he could win.

Stung into action at last, Luke seized his lightsaber and turned to strike Palpatine down, but Darth Vader's lightsaber blocked him. The Emperor's sickening, triumphant laugh echoed through the chamber as Luke and Darth Vader duelled once more.

On Endor, the Ewoks were winning the battle. At last Han and Leia were able to rush into the shield generator. They could only hope they would be able to destroy it in time.

Luke threw Darth Vader down a flight of steps... then stopped. All at once he realised where his lack of control was leading him. He hid, but his feelings betrayed him. Darth Vader at last sensed the existence of Leia and threatened to turn her to the dark side.

Luke lost his temper again. He rushed at Darth Vader with such rage that he knocked him back, and with a furious swipe of his lightsaber he cut off his father's right hand. The Emperor laughed in delight and encouraged Luke to kill his father. But Luke was horrified by what he had done. Turning to face the eager Palpatine, he swore once and for all that he would never turn to the dark side.

The Emperor finally accepted that he could not turn Luke. Instead, he flung the full extent of his Force power against the young Jedi. Sith lightning crackled from his fingers, flinging Luke to the ground in agony, unable to move or speak.

At last the strike team on Endor blew up the shield generator and the shield was destroyed. Seizing his one chance, Lando flew the *Millennium Falcon* into the heart of the Death Star. He locked his weapons on to the power generator and hurtled towards it, pursued by Imperial fighters.

Darth Vader rose to his feet and watched his son writhing on the floor. Inside the heart of the Sith Lord, Anakin Skywalker was struggling to break free – the Anakin who had been a brother to Obi-Wan, who had loved Padmé, who had become a hero for his valiant deeds during the Clone Wars. Intent on torturing Luke, the Emperor was not paying attention to his apprentice.

At last Vader made up his mind. He turned to the Emperor, lifted him high into the air as if he weighed no more than a feather, and flung him down the power shaft, still crackling with the dark power of the Force that he had generated. Palpatine and all his evil perished in a dazzling explosion of blue lightning.

Fatally wounded by the Emperor's Sith lightning, Anakin Skywalker collapsed to the floor and Luke rushed to his side.

Luke carried his father to the landing platform and gently removed his mask. At last he looked into the face of Anakin Skywalker, white, scarred and hideous – a mockery of the handsome young man who Padmé had fallen in love with. But Luke saw only love in Anakin's tired, scarred eyes. Anakin had been saved, and he died in his son's arms.

On the *Millennium Falcon*, Lando fired on the main power generator and the Death Star began to explode from within. He escaped just in time and Luke escaped on board a small fighter. The Death Star blew up into tiny pieces behind them.

Later that day, across the galaxy, every city and settlement on every planet celebrated the end of the Empire. There was still a great deal to do and a huge amount to be rebuilt, but at long last the evil that had rotted the heart of the galaxy had been destroyed.

JABBA THE HUTT

Jabba the Hutt was a gangster who ruled a vast criminal empire from his desert palace on Tatooine. He was an unforgiving and sadistic crime lord. His palace was always filled with ruthless criminals and he was involved in every illegal enterprise that plagued the Outer Rim.

MEMORABLE DATES

600 BBY - Jabba the Hutt born

58 BBY - Arrives on Tatooine

32 BBY - Sponsors the Boonta Eve Podrace

4 ABY - Dies at the hands of Princess Leia

A -hideous, slug-like creature, Jabba was a pitiless and sadistic crime lord, whose notorious criminal empire was masterminded from his desert palace on Tatooine. During the Clone Wars, he granted the Republic passage through Hutt-controlled hyperspace lanes to show his gratitude for the rescue of his son, Rotta. However, in the absence of any moral rudder, his choices were ruled by greed alone.

Jabba's father was a major clan leader and member of a long line of criminal masterminds, which is why Jabba's greatest ambition was to become his father's equal. By the time he was 600 years-old, Jabba had forged a major crime ring.

He moved from his father's private estate on Nal Hutta to the desert planet of Tatooine, where he built a palace out of the ancient monastery of the B'omarr monks.

After moving to Tatooine, Jabba amassed an even larger fortune through illegal activities such as smuggling, glitterstim spice dealing, assassination, loan sharking and protection. He controlled the majority of the planet's cities, towns, and spaceports. He had no scruples about the activities that made him money, condoning anything from piracy to slavery if it lined his pockets. The famed decadence of Jabba's palace soon attracted vast numbers of parasitic revellers, who only wanted to drink, eat and be entertained. Thieves, smugglers, assassins, spies and all manner of criminals were always at Jabba's side, enjoying his cruel sense of humour... and sometimes suffering from it. Jabba's only thought in life was greed, and as vile as his outward form was, it could never compare in ugliness or horror to his putrid character.

CHEWBACCA

The Wookiee Chewbacca was very loyal and as strong as a gladiator. He had a varied and exciting life, for he spent time as a respected soldier, a slave, a smuggler and a skilled pilot and mechanic.

MEMORABLE DATES

200 BBY - Chewbacca born
19 BBY - Battle of Kashyyyk
0 - Battle of Yavin
3 ABY - Battle of Hoth
4 ABY - Battle of Endor
25 ABY - Chewbacca dies

Loyal, strong and insightful, the tall Wookiee was a true hero of the Rebellion as well as a good friend to its leaders. Although Chewbacca's initial involvement in the Rebellion was due to Han Solo, his connection to the Empire stretched back to a time before Luke or Leia were born... back to Chewbacca's home planet of Kashyyyk.

As a Wookiee warrior, Chewbacca served under the command of Jedi Master Yoda in the Clone Wars. Separatist forces had invaded his beautiful homeworld of Kashyyyk, where cities were suspended high above the forest floor. Determined to defend their jungle planet, Chewbacca and fellow warrior Tarfful prepared for battle.

Yoda had developed a good relationship with the mighty Wookiees, earning their respect and affection. They served Yoda faithfully, but their most crucial moment came when Palpatine gave Order 66. Chewbacca displayed the ferocity and courage that Wookiees are known for, and helped General Yoda escape a surprise ambush.

He was not a Jedi and he was certainly not a pacifist. He could tear the limbs off most creatures barehanded. He carried a bowcaster, a crossbow-like weapon that shot explosive packets of energy, and could have taken on a squad of stormtroopers. Chewbacca appeared brave and fearless, and his courage often inspired others to greater feats. But sometimes his terrifying growls and roars hid his fear of the unknown.

After the defeat of the Jedi, Chewbacca was badly mistreated and eventually saved from certain death by a young smuggler called Han Solo. The Wookiee promised a 'life debt' to Solo, and their subsequent adventures together became the stuff of legend.

GALAXY QUIZ

PART 6

COMPLETE THIS FINAL PART OF THE QUIZ AND
THEN ADD UP YOUR SCORES TO DISCOVER HOW
KNOWLEDGEABLE YOU REALLY ARE!

1. Who killed Qui-Gon Jinn?

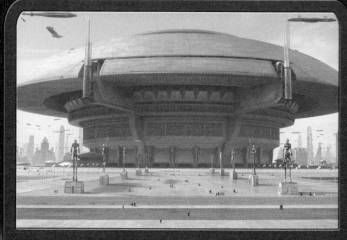

**3. On which planet did the
Clone Wars end?**

**2. Who was the Viceroy of the
Trade Federation?**

**4. Who tried to assassinate
Senator Padmé Amidala?**

5. What was the name of Han Solo's ship?

9. On which planet did Princess Leia tell Grand Moff Tarkin that the Rebels were hiding?

6. What was the Emperor's Sith name?

10. Who helped Han Solo and his strike team destroy the shield generator on Endor?

7. What kind of planet is Kashyyyk?

ADD YOUR SCORE TO YOUR OVERALL TOTAL.
THEN CHECK TO SEE HOW YOU HAVE FARED!

60–73 – Congratulations, you know a great deal about the history of the galaxy, and your wisdom and insight are remarkable for one so young. You will be a valuable addition to the Jedi Order. Remember to practise patience and self-control, and allow the Force to flow through you.

40–59 – Through a combination of luck, wit and arrogance you have achieved a reasonable result, but the Force indicates that there may be grave danger in your future. Forget your desire for personal glory and think only of the Force.

1–39 – There is so much fear in you that it overpowers everything you do. Before you can become a Jedi Knight, you must learn to trust the Force and listen to your instincts.

8. Who killed Greedo?

Check your answers on page 110/111 and add up your score.
(You will always get one point for every correct answer.)

TOTAL SCORE FOR GALAXY QUIZ PART 6

ANSWERS

PAGE 18

Chancellor Palpatine is the odd one out, because he is the only one who has never duelled with Obi-Wan Kenobi.

PAGE 19

THE REBELS WILL RENDEZVOUS AT 0800 HOURS AT THE OUTER RIM.
LUKE SKYWALKER WILL LEAD THE SQUADRON.
PRINCESS LEIA IS CARRYING THE PLANS OF THE DEATH STAR.

PAGES 20

1. Name: Chewbacca
   Species: Wookiee
2. Name: Jar Jar Binks
   Species: Gungan
3. Name: Jabba the Hutt
   Species: Hutt
4. Name: Ki-Adi-Mundi
   Species: Cerean
5. Name: Plo Koon
   Species: Kel Dor
6. Name: Watto
   Species: Toydarian
7. Name: Admiral Ackbar
   Species: Mon Calamari
8. Name: Wicket W. Warrick
   Species: Ewok
9. Name: Boba Fett
   Species: Human
10. Name: Lama Su
    Species: Kaminoan

PAGE 36

KILLALLJEDI (across)
KAMINO (down)
POKKORON (down)
TATOOINE (across)
DARTH (down)
GEONOSIS (down)
JANGOFETT (across)
GRIEVOUS (down)
LIGHTSABER (across)
SIDIOUS (down)
MUSTAFAR (across)
COUNTDOOKU (across)

PAGE 37

GEONOSIS

NABOO

KAMINO

CORUSCANT

TATOOINE

HOTH

ENDOR

YAVIN

PAGES 38

1. Qui-Gon Jinn
2. Jar-Jar Binks
3. Darth Maul
4. Naboo
5. AT-TE walker
6. Watto
7. It was high in midi-chlorians
8. Zam Wesell
9. Three
10. Sebulba
11. Tusken Raiders
12. Anakin Skywalker – Darth Vader
13. General Grievous
14. Nute Gunray
15. Princess Leia